WHAT'S WRONG
CIVILIZASHU

*The 'William' books re-published with
the original illustrations by Thomas Henry*

1 JUST – WILLIAM
2 MORE WILLIAM
3 WILLIAM AGAIN
4 WILLIAM THE FOURTH
5 STILL – WILLIAM
6 WILLIAM THE CONQUEROR
7 WILLIAM – THE OUTLAW
8 WILLIAM – IN TROUBLE
9 WILLIAM – THE GOOD
10 WILLIAM
11 WILLIAM – THE BAD
12 WILLIAM'S HAPPY DAYS
13 WILLIAM'S CROWDED HOURS
14 WILLIAM – THE PIRATE
15 WILLIAM – THE REBEL
16 WILLIAM – THE GANGSTER
17 WILLIAM – THE DETECTIVE
18 SWEET WILLIAM
19 WILLIAM – THE SHOWMAN
20 WILLIAM – THE DICTATOR
21 WILLIAM AND AIR RAID PRECAUTIONS
22 WILLIAM AND THE EVACUEES
23 WILLIAM DOES HIS BIT
24 WILLIAM CARRIES ON
25 WILLIAM AND THE BRAINS TRUST
26 JUST WILLIAM'S LUCK

Also available

JUST – WILLIAM
a facsimile of the first (1922) edition

For publication in 1990:

THE WILLIAM COMPANION
by Mary Cadogan

JUST WILLIAM'S WORLD – A PICTORIAL MAP
by Gillian Clements and Kenneth Waller

What's Wrong with Civilizashun

and other important ritings

by

William Brown
(and Richmal Crompton)

With a foreword by
Mary Cadogan

MACMILLAN

Text copyright © Richmal Ashbee
What's Wrong with Civilizashun © 1990 Richmal Ashbee
Illustrations copyright © The Thomas Henry Fisher Estate

The following articles were first published in *The Happy Mag* between 1927 and 1933:
'Something Like a Change', 'New Year's Day', 'The Job I'd Like Best', 'School Is a Waste
of Time', 'William's Christmas Presents', 'Christmas Day with William', 'Home for the
Holidays', 'I'll Tell You What's Wrong with Christmas', 'Commonsense about Holidays' and
'My Summer Holiday'.

'My Day in London' first appeared in *Tit-Bits*

'What's Wrong with Civilizashun' is, the publishers believe, published here for the first
time.

This collection first published 1990 by
MACMILLAN CHILDREN'S BOOKS
A division of Macmillan Publishers Limited
London and Basingstoke
Associated companies throughout the world

ISBN 0-333-52656-2

A CIP catalogue record for this book is available from
the British Library

Printed and bound in Great Britain by Billing & Sons Ltd, Worcester

Acknowledgement

The publishers wish to thank David Schutte for the loan of copies of *The Happy Mag* and for his help in compiling this collection.

Contents

Foreword

Richmal Crompton sometimes described William Brown as her 'Frankenstein's Monster'. When she started writing about him she had no intention of producing the several hundred stories which now make up the thirty-eight William books. However, William became so popular that she was persuaded to write more and more of his adventures. Eventually the inevitable happened: it seemed to Richmal that William was actually telling her what to write.

Richmal once said, ' . . . For many years I looked on William as "my character". He was my puppet. I pulled his strings. But gradually the tables have been turned. I am his puppet. He pulls the strings. For he is resolute, indomitable and inclined to be tyrannical . . . He refuses to co-operate in some plots. He makes fantastic demands on others . . . '

In the stories William makes it emphatically clear that he prefers playing out of doors to reading – indeed, that he does not consider 'there's a single book that needs to have been written'. Nevertheless he still saw himself as an author, and several of the books tell us that he wrote stories and plays. These were accounts of ghosts and luminous skeletons, rattling chains and secret passages, or epic adventures of kidnap and hidden treasure featuring a pirate called Dick of the Bloody Hand. William firmly declared that his work was a 'jolly sight more in'restin' than Shakespeare'. (He also expressed the hope that if any book he had written was ever published, it would have 'a picture of a big splash of blood on the back' because this would 'make anyone want to read it'!)

William (or rather Richmal Crompton) is the author of *What's Wrong with Civilizashun*, which comprises articles and diary entries originally produced for publication in magazines, and here collected in book form for the first time.

In fact, nearly all the stories which appear in the other thirty-eight books were also first written for periodicals. *The Happy Mag* was one of the best known of these. Lively and colourful, it was designed for adults but many children read it too, because of the William adventures. For several years Richmal Crompton wrote these stories every month for *The Happy Mag*, and they were illustrated by Thomas Henry, whose pictures of William are so familiar to us all. William became so popular that the publishers decided to issue collections of the stories in book form.

However, readers still wanted more of William, so it was decided that further items (by William himself) should appear in *The Happy Mag*. You will see from *What's Wrong with Civilizashun* that Richmal sometimes allowed William to write in his characteristic style, but sometimes corrected his spelling and grammar (after all she was once a schoolmistress). Younger readers in particular will enjoy spotting these variations, as well as William's historical and political howlers. Because these articles were written some time ago, they will also notice that William talks about 'the king' and not 'the queen'; about steam trains; about uncomfortable clothes (for example, collars with studs) which fortunately children today do not have to wear; and about 'old' money (when a penny could buy *very* much more than it can now). All this, of course, adds flavour and interest to William's 'ritings'. He claims in *What's Wrong with Civilizashun* that people who read his literary creations find them 'exciting'. I'm sure that you will do so too!

Mary Cadogan

WHAT'S WRONG WITH CIVILIZASHUN

What's Wrong with Civilizashun

Sometimes you see things in the papers about what's wrong with civilizashun an' how it could be put right an' that sort of thing an' it seems to me that people that write them are all talking through their hats because they go on an' on tryin' to find out what's wrong with civilizashun an' what they never seem to see is that civilizashun's all wrong anyway an' that nothing will ever be right till we all go back to bein' savages.

I've thought a good deal about this an' I bet I know more about it than anyone else 'cause I've thought about it more. Ever since I can remember I've thought that civilizashun was all wrong an' I've wanted to be a savage. I can never understand how people can go on bein' civilized when they could so easily turn into savages. If I were the king I'd make everyone stop bein' civilized an' start bein' savages again an' I bet we'd all be a jolly sight happier.

1

Take houses to start with. Savages didn't have houses. They had caves an' caves are a jolly sight better than houses any day. You don't have to wipe your feet before you go into caves an' there aren't any ornaments to knock over or carpets to get muddy or things to get sticky if you only jus' put a finger on them by accident like what there are in houses. The way people fill their houses with things that aren't any use to anyone an' that break or get finger marked almost with lookin' at has always been a myst'ry to me.

Then their food wasn't dull like what civilized food is — potatoes an' milk pudding an' bread an' butter an' stuff like that. I bet prehistoric animals tasted jolly good an' they cooked them themselves over fires an' I know that stuff you cook yourself over fires tastes better than any other sort of food 'cause I've often tried it. I once made a mixture of sardines an' blackberries an' sherbert an' liquorice water an' cooked it over a fire an' it tasted jolly good though people will never believe it did.

Then savages didn't have all this silly fuss about washing their hands before meals an' eating with knives an' forks an' spoons an' things. They jus' ate with their fingers same as I always find it easiest to an' their meals must have been much jollier than what ours are with no one goin' on an' on at them all the time telling them not to stick their elbows out an' not to talk with their mouths full an' things like that. Then with the time they saved with not having to wipe their feet an' wash their hands every minute they'd time to do really int'resting things like chasing prehistoric animals over rocks an' such like.

Then they dressed much more sensibly than what we do. F'rinstance you can't imagine a savage wearing a collar an' tie 'cause they'd jolly well got more sense. It always seems to me that collars must have been invented by someone that had been annoyed by boys an' wanted to avenge himself on them 'cause they get dirty the minute you put them on an' then everyone starts goin' on at you again an' saying why can't you keep it clean for two minutes an' things like that. An' then the stud's always breaking or coming out or getting lost an' your collar gets round to under your ear or you've used your tie to mend something an' they all start goin' on at you again. I think that if a savage could see us wearing collars an' studs an' ties he'd fairly split himself with laughing an' he'd feel jolly glad that he'd had the sense not to get civilized. I'd sooner dress in the skins of animals I'd killed any day than in collars an' studs an' ties an' waistcoats an' things like that that I can't see any sense in.

Then there's manners which is another thing that's a great mistake an' that we waste a lot of valu'ble time over such as saying how do you do to people when we don't care how they do an' shaking hands an' opening doors for girls and fetching trifle for them at parties till by the time they give us a minute to get something ourselves there's no trifle left. Savages didn't do things like that. They had too much sense.

I bet if there was any trifle goin' at one of their parties, they jolly well ate it themselves an' made the girls have jelly an' jolly sens'ble of them, too. An' I bet if a savage feels like putting his tongue out at someone he jolly well puts it out without his mother telling him he was disgracing her an' if he feels like smacking someone's head he jolly well smacks it without being told that he isn't behaving like a gentleman. He has a jolly good time goin' about with a stick club an' fightin' everyone he meets when he isn't chasing prehistoric animals over rocks.

That's what makes me feel so wild when I think how I'm spending the best years of my life in school learning things that wouldn't be any use to me even if I did learn them when I might be going out with a club dressed in skins an' fighting everyone I met an' chasing prehistoric animals over rocks. I'd like to see a savage sitting down to do sums about simple interest and French exercises about where is the spade of the gardener of my aunt. I bet he'd soon be chasing the maths master an' the French master round the room with his club which is what I often jolly well want to do myself.

People talk of the wonderful inventions of civilizashun but I don't think they're so wonderful myself. Take printing

The best years of my life.

f'rinstance an' think of all the dull books that are printed about hist'ry an' g'ography an' arithmetic an' stuff like that that we've got to waste our valu'ble time over instead of going out fighting our enemies with clubs an' chasing prehistoric animals over rocks. Then there are the sort of books that people get for prizes called heroes of roman hist'ry an' gasses of the atmosphere an' wonders of nature an' stuff like that. I don't feel so mad about that of course as some people do because I've never had a prize an' from what people tell me I'm never likely to an' what's more I jolly well don't want to. What I want to do is to be a savage an' fancy a savage dressed in an eton suit walking up to a little platform to bow to a fat bishop an' get gasses of the atmosphere given him.

When people say that we ought to be grateful for great inventions like printing I say that I'm jolly well not going to be grateful for something that's made our lives miserable with decimals an' fractions an' dates an' exports an' imports an' spades of the gardener of my aunt an' things like that. I don't think there's a single book that need have been printed. There are some exciting tales of course but I can make up as exciting tales as you ever see printed.

I once made up a tale about a man that was taken captive by cannibals an' got away by jumping out of the pot they'd put him in to boil an' snatching up the pepper jar an' sprinkling it over them an' then while they were all sneezing diving into the river and swimming under water till he came to the sea. Once a shark got hold of him but he took out his pen knife and cut off the shark's head still swimming under water and when he got to the sea he was captured by pirates an' made to walk the plank an' when he got to the end of it he made a spring an' caught hold of an aeroplane that was passing over the ship an' well, I won't go on any more but there was pages an' pages of it all jus' like that an' I bet none of you have read a printed book half as exciting. Everyone that read it said it was the most exciting tale they'd ever read but most people said they couldn't read it. A lot of people are very bad at reading my writing.

Then think of trains. People say that trains are a wonderful invention an' that we're better off than savages because of trains.

I don't think that trains are a bit exciting. People won't let you
do anything int'resting in them. They won't let you see how
far you can hang out of the window or pull down the chain
thing to stop it or open the door to walk along the little ledge
to the next carriage while the train's going which looks quite
easy an' I know I could do it if only people would leave me
alone. They won't even let you try swinging along the luggage
rack that couldn't possibly do anyone any harm or play at being
a red indian under the seat. For all the fun they let you have in
a train you might as well be sitting in a room at home.

The only people who get any fun out of a train are the engine
drivers an' they're generally very bad tempered men an' turn
you out of the engine quite savagely if ever you manage to get
in to see how it works. People say that trains are a blessing to
us because we can go an' see our relations in them but all I can
say is that people who feel like that must have jolly different
relations to what I have. If I was a savage I wouldn't have to
go an' see my aunts an' anyway if I wanted to I'd go on a wild
horse an' I bet a wild horse is a jolly sight more exciting than a
train to ride on. I once said this to someone an' they said that
a wild horse would never go to the place you wanted it to go
but I said that that would only make it more exciting. Fancy
setting off on a wild horse to see your aunt an' ending up in
the heart of an undiscovered jungle.

Then there's the telephone. People talk a lot about the
telephone an' what a wonderful invention it is an' all that sort
of thing but I've always found the telephone's the opposite to a
blessing. People are always ringing up your father to complain
of you going into their garden for your ball an' treading on
their flower beds by mistake or taking a short cut through
their garden when you're being chased by your enemies which
you'd have thought anyone decent would be glad for you to
do. If the telephone hadn't been invented they'd have had to
come round to see your father or else written a letter an' ten to
one they'd have forgotten or it would have been raining or they
wouldn't have had a stamp or your father would have been out or
something. A telephone doesn't give you a sporting chance.

Then there's electricity. People say that that's a blessing but all I can say to that is that the people who say that don't know anything about it. I know more about electricity than most people do because once I tried to turn our electric iron into an electric train and I was nearly killed by it and I've thought ever since then that electricity was very dangerous and ought never to have been invented.

I haven't time to go through many more inventions but there's photography which is one of the worst and a thing that savages were lucky not to have to put up with having your neck and

ears nearly scrubbed off and a clean collar on an' then sitting on an uncomfortable chair and people going on an' on at you telling you not to scowl and to smile an' look pleasant and then when you do smile saying no good gracious not like that and then when the prints come everyone saying doesn't he look awful he must have moved. That's one of the times I long to be turned into a savage with a club.

I don't think much of motor cars either. I'd sooner have a wild horse any day. The fuss they make about them saying don't stand on the seats or leave the lights alone or come away from the tool box or stop blowing the horn when all you're doing is just taking a little int'rest in the thing that anyone decent would be glad for you to do. I was jus' looking at one outside our house one day when suddenly it started off and went right down the hill and into a ditch. They said I must have taken the brake off but I don't see how I could have done because I only just moved a few things here and there to see how it worked. Anyway they made one of the most awful fusses that I've ever had made at me and I've disliked motor cars ever since. I don't like the people who drive them either. When they nearly run over you they always shout at you as if it was your fault and as if you hadn't got the right to play in the road in your own village. I'd like to chase them all with a club on a wild horse same as I'd be able to if I was a savage.

I could write a lot more about this but I've not got time just now, because Ginger's waiting for me to go out to play with him. I votes we play savages. Jumble makes a fine prehistoric animal and there's a goat in Farmer Jenks's field that makes a jolly fine wild horse but it all depends whether Farmer Jenks sees us or not. Anyway we can make a fire in the woods an' cook something on it. I want to try cooking a mixture of sausage an' jam an' ice cream an' peanuts an' nougat. I got the sausage an' jam out of the larder when no one was looking. I think it ought to taste jolly nice.

Something Like a Change!
New Views on Holiday Problems

I'd make everyone's fathers go to school all through the holidays.

I heard someone say the other day that people ought to do the opposite sort of things from the things they usually do on a holiday, and I've been thinking about it a good deal and it seems to me that it's very sensible, and I only wish that people would. In fact, the more I think about it the more sensible it seems, and if they'd only let me arrange it I'd make a sort of holiday that would do everyone a lot of good.

For one thing I'd have schools all kept open, and I'd make everyone's fathers go to school all through the holidays and have them treated there just as we're treated. I don't mean, of course, that I think that people's fathers would actually enjoy this, because, of course, they wouldn't, but I think that it would do them a lot of good and make them much more sympathetic than what they are now.

For instance, when I went home and told my father that I'd been cruelly treated at school, my father, because he'd been cruelly treated himself by the same people last holidays, would write the sort of letter to them that I often try to get him to write, instead of just saying 'Serve you right' and silly things like that. And if I wanted to be too ill to go to school on a day when I hadn't had time to do my homework, my father would understand, instead of sending for the doctor and making me drink beastly medicine. In fact, I think that it would make fathers much more helpful altogether, because all the term time they'd be trying to get their own back on the masters for all that they'd made them suffer in the holidays, and so they'd be much more useful to their sons than what they are at present.

I like to think of my father setting off to find the head master and treat him as he's treated me. At present, of course, I can't imagine it, but if he'd been through the same sufferings last holidays, he'd probably be glad to avenge me, because he'd be avenging himself at the same time.

I think that their reports at the end of the holidays ought to be sent in to us, and I bet they'd be jolly rotten ones, because they never seem to know the answer to any question you ask them in homework. Then when our reports came to them at the end of term they wouldn't be able to say anything because they'd know that theirs would be just as bad at the end of the holidays.

I think that fathers would be much nicer and easier to get on with if this were done than what they are now. And if it made them take their children away from school so as not to have to go to school themselves in the holidays, it would be a very good thing.

Then I think that mothers ought to have a change from housekeeping. I often hear my mother say how tired she gets of ordering meals, but when I offer to do it for her, she'll never let me, so she can't be as tired of it as she makes out. Anyway, I'd make all mothers have a change from ordering meals, and I'd make the children do it instead, and I bet they'd do it a jolly sight better.

It's extraordinary to me what dull food we get when our mothers order it – milk puddings and stewed prunes and beef and mutton and things like that. They'd see a jolly big difference when we took it over. I'd have ice cream and sherbet (as much as anyone could eat) for breakfast, and for lunch I'd have cream buns and chocolate eclairs and macaroons and strawberries and cream and liquorice water to drink.

For tea I'd have a cake – I don't know what it's called, but it's made to look like a cauliflower, and all the inside is cream and the outside green marzipan. I'd have dozens and dozens of them so that everyone could eat as many as they liked. I wouldn't have any bread and butter at all.

Then, for supper, I'd have trifle made mostly with cream and banana squash, which is a mixture of banana and strawberry jam and cream, and chocolate biscuits, and ice cream and raspberryade to drink. It would save a lot of money on meat and potatoes and bread and things like that, as well as being much nicer. I bet father would like it when he came home from school. At least, he would if he'd any sense.

Then when I was looking after the house for my mother, I'd have things made a bit different in it. I'd have all the flowerbeds taken away from the garden because it's impossible to have any fun in a garden that's full of flowerbeds. You can't have really good games. If you try to, everyone makes a terrible fuss because you've trodden on a few flowers. I'd make the garden just nice rough grass with a few trees.

I wouldn't have any ornaments in the house because there isn't any sense in them and I'd only have a few chairs to sit down on and one table to eat meals at and nothing else, because a lot of furniture only gets in your way when you're playing games. In fact, I don't think that I'd have even a table to eat meals at, because I think it's much more fun having meals out-of-doors or in a barn or in a tool-shed, or somewhere like that if it's raining out-of-doors.

I'd sell sweets a great deal cheaper – and of course I'd eat a good deal
many myself!

Then I think that the shopkeepers ought to have a change
from shopkeeping in the holidays, especially in the sweet-shops.
I think that the boys ought to take over the sweet-shops for them
while they're having the change. We could easily go down to the
sweet-shops when we'd ordered the ice cream and other things
for the meals. I think that the sweet-shop keepers charge far
too much money for their sweets. I'd sell them a good deal
cheaper, and I'd eat a good deal many myself, of course, because
a shopkeeper has to do that to stop them getting stale.

I think the doctors all ought to have a change too. We could
take on their work. I've often thought I'd like to be a doctor.
I could easily just shut up my sweet-shop for an hour or two
while I went round to see people that were ill, and tell them
to stay in bed and give them medicine. I bet I could make as

nasty medicine as our doctor makes. I'd have a jolly good try anyhow.

I hope our doctor will be ill and I have to give him medicine. I think that would be great fun. It would make him very careful how he treated me the next time I was ill. I bet he'd give me medicine that tasted a bit better after that. And it would be fun punching people all over, and saying 'Does that hurt?' And they wouldn't be allowed to punch you back, because you're a doctor.

Then, of course, there's engine drivers, and I certainly think that they ought to have a change and someone else to take on their engines. I wouldn't mind driving their engines for them, because I'd probably want a change from the sweet-shop and other things some day.

We could do it in turns. One day I could have the sweet-shop, and Ginger be a doctor, and Henry an engine driver, and Douglas something else. Then the next day we could all change round. I'd take one of those big bottles of bulls' eyes with me when I was an engine driver to eat on the way. I'd have great fun shovelling in coal and getting black all over.

I'd have a fine time driving buses.

I'd start it before its time sometimes, too, because it's such fun to see people running along with bags and things in their hands after a train that's just going out of a station. Then, of course, there's buses. I'd have a fine time driving buses and going past stopping places without stopping.

Then when the holidays were over and we went to school, and all the other people went back to their ordinary work, everyone would have had a nice change – especially us – and would be longing for the next holidays to come along. I don't suppose they'll ever do all this, but I think that it would be great fun if they did.

Christmas Day
with William

Turn on light to look at Christmas presents.

5.0 Wake up. Remember that it's Christmas Day. Feel stocking. Seems pretty full, but you can't tell from that. People have a mean way of filling it up with apples and oranges, and things like that that one can have every day and that oughtn't to count as Christmas presents at all.

6.0 Wake up again. Remember again that it's Christmas Day. Turn on light to look at Christmas presents. Nothing very interesting. A tie, a tin of sweets, a box of crayons, a penknife, a mouth organ, a box of plasticine. The box of plasticine from Aunt Jane. It's a wonder she didn't give me a rattle. Anyway, it's better than the history book she gave me last year. All the bottom part of the stocking filled up with oranges and apples

and nuts as usual – which seems to me just the same as cheating.
I quite like oranges and apples and nuts, of course, but it seems
mean to make Christmas presents of them. I've a good mind to
give all of them a nut each for their presents next year and
see how they like it.

6.15– 6.20 Sweets very good.

6.20– 6.25 Apples very good.

6.25– 6.35 Nuts very good. Saved a few nuts for later in the
day. Mouth organ very good, but before I've had a real try at
it everyone shouts at me to shut up. They all sound very cross.
I'll wait till a little later before I try again. Think how funny it
is that people always get cross on Christmas Day.

6.40 Take out my presents for people: a book for my father
called 'A Redskin's Revenge', a bag of Liquorice All Sorts for
my mother, a pistol for Robert, and a whistle for Ethel. With
luck they'll give me them back at once, but if they don't I'll wait
a few days and then pinch them back without saying anything.
I've got calendars for Aunt Jane and Uncle George. They're
very good calendars, and I took a lot of trouble choosing the
nicest ones that came for my mother last week. Get the things
ready that I've bought to try and make things jolly. Sometimes
things are very dull on Christmas Day, so I always try to have a
few things ready to make it more lively. This time I've got some
squibs and a mask and a box of tricks. It's a jolly good mask –
a black face with an awful grin on it – and the box of tricks is a
jolly good one, too. The spilled ink and jam are very old ones, of
course, but they generally seem to come off, and there's a thing
that lifts up people's plates when you squeeze something, and
a camera that squirts water in people's faces. They're all great
fun and help to make a party jolly that's getting dull.

6.45 Think that everyone must be awake now, so begin
practising on my mouth organ again. Everyone yells out to
me to stop again. They still sound very cross.

7.0 Wake up and find I've been to sleep again. Begin singing 'Christians, Awake'. They yell out at me again and sound crosser than ever. That's the sort of reward you always get when you try to give people a little pleasure. Had another look at my presents. Don't like the colour of my tie. It's a nasty sort of yellow. Try to make it blue by rubbing green crayon on to it. It doesn't make it blue, but they're jolly good crayons. Draw a big red spider on the wall – the best spider I've ever drawn. Draw a black skeleton next to it. I'm jolly good at spiders and skeletons. Do a row of spiders and skeletons all in different colours. They look jolly fine.

7.15 Hear cook coming downstairs. Put on my mask and look out of my door as she passes. She screams and falls downstairs. Seems as if my mask was going to be a great success helping to make things jolly.

I'll give him a nut to cheer him up.

7.25 Hear Robert go into the bathroom, so begin to get up. While washing, draw row of spiders and skeletons on window with soap to cheer people up passing along the road outside. See a very cross-looking man coming down the road. Think I'll give him a nut to cheer him up. Throw one to him, using garter as a catapult. Jolly good shot. Hits him just under his

ear. Shakes his fist at me and shouts out something about telling my father. It's funny how people simply won't be cheered
up, however hard you try.

Try making myself look like an Arab Chieftain by wrapping
bath towel round me. Looks jolly fine, except that my face looks
a bit too pale. Go to Robert's room – Robert still in bathroom
– and take the cork from his bottle of hair-oil. Burn it with a
match and give myself a moustache. It looks jolly fine, but my
hair looks all wrong. Fetch bottle of hair-oil – Robert still in
bathroom – and make my hair stick up in spikes all over my
head. Don't know if Arab Chieftains really wear their hair in
spikes, but it's a jolly good way of wearing it. It looks savage
and exciting.

7.45 Someone knocks at my door and says, am I getting up?
I say, yes, I am, a happy Christmas, and they say it won't be a
very happy one if I go on kicking up a row with that mouth organ
all day. So I say, all right, keep your hair on, and start washing
again because the moustache has got all over my face.

8.0 Robert back from his bath, banging about and shouting
that his hair-oil's gone. Says it was there before he went for his
bath. Everyone says it couldn't have been, and why can't he
take better care of his things? He's always losing something and,
anyway, he needn't make such a fuss about it. In between saying
these things, they all wish each other a happy Christmas.

8.5 Kindly threw another nut to a boy going down the road.
Another jolly good shot. Caught him on the top of his head.
He chucked a stone back at me that came right in at the open
window, but I'd ducked just in time. Decided to keep that garter
for a catapult. It makes a jolly good one.

8.20 Hear mother go downstairs and cook telling her that
she had a vision as she passed my room of an awful black face
looking out, and she hopes it doesn't mean that harm's coming

to me. Mother says that it means more likely that harm's coming to other people. Robert still going on and on about his hair-oil. Father tells him for heaven's sake to shut up and lends him his. They wish each other a happy Christmas.

8.30 Breakfast bell rings. Suddenly realise that there'll be a row about spiders and skeletons on wall paper. Try to wipe it off with towel. Not successful. Soap nail brush well and try to scrub it off. Worse still. Have a brainy idea and try to cover it up with pieces of plasticine nearly the same colour as the wall paper.

Great fun doing this. Plasticine rather jolly stuff. Cover nose with red plasticine just to see what it looks like. Looks awfully funny. Someone calls up, am I ever coming down? Take red plasticine off nose and brush spikes out of hair. Get Christmas presents and go downstairs.

8.40 Wish everyone a happy Christmas and give presents. Mother and Father quite decent and give 'A Redskin's Revenge' and Liquorice All Sorts back to me at once. Robert and Ethel very mean and pretend they wanted pistol and whistle. Evidently intend to stick to them just to annoy me. Just like them. Give calendars to Aunt Jane and Uncle George. They thank me, but not very much. Find I'd forgotten to scratch out the To Mrs. Brown on the other sides. As if one had time to think of everything!

Uncle George gave me box with gummed labels, drawing pins, rubber rings and tube of glue, and says that he's got one just like it and has always found it very useful, and it's time I learnt to be methodical and helpful. Thank him, but not very much. Wonder whether to ask Ethel to swop it for the whistle, but decide not to. It might come in useful, especially the glue, and anyway mean to get the whistle back whether she gives it to me or not.

9.15 Ethel goes into garden and sees spiders and skeletons soaped on to my window that I'd forgotten to wipe off. Comes in and makes an awful fuss about it. Someone goes up to wash it off. Awful fuss about plasticine and marks on wall.

9.20 Remind them that Christmas is supposed to be time of peace and good will, but this only makes them worse. Go out for walk to give them time to get over it.

9.30 Meet Ginger, who says his people are being as disagreeable as mine, because of a trumpet and a box of chemicals he'd had for Christmas presents. He'd been practising the trumpet in the early morning quite quietly and he'd spilt one of the bottles out of his box of chemicals over a table of his mother's and it had burnt a hole in it. He can't see why they're making such a fuss about it, because he's often heard his mother tell people that it's over a hundred years old, so it's about time she got a new one, anyway.

9.45 Come home and find Robert making an awful fuss, because he's just found his hair-oil in my room with bits of burnt cork floating in it. He says he can't possibly use it now and calls me so many names that mother says hush, hush, dear. I know he's very trying, but remember it's Christmas Day.
Then he says, one thing I can be quite sure of is that I jolly well won't see that pistol I gave him again, because he's going to give it to the first boy he sees, and goes straight out and gives it to Peter Greenall who's just passing the gate, going to see his grandmother and give her a bow and arrow that he's wanted a long time for her Christmas present. Which is rather a good joke, because I can lick Peter Greenall any day and I bet I have the pistol back first thing to-morrow.

10.0 Mother says that Aunt Jane's rather hurt because I'm not wearing the tie she gave me, and I must put it on for church. Go up to put it on, but forget it's crayoned till I come down and everyone starts going on at me because my collar's all green. Go up to change collar.

10.30 Go to church. Sermon about being kind to people. Look at my family and hope they're taking it in, but none of them seem to be listening.

1.0 Only allowed two helpings of turkey and three of plum pudding which seems rather mean but got the sixpence out of the pudding. Jolly good dinner on the whole.

2.0 Everyone goes to lie down. Think I'll have a nice quiet practice on my mouth organ now there's no one to disturb; but the minute I begin everyone starts yelling at me from upstairs to stop. Wonder why they can't get on with their lying down instead of interfering with me all the time? Ask them what there is for me to do if I can't practise my mouth organ. Mother says play quietly with your other things.

2.10 Play quietly with my other things. Find that that box Uncle George gave me isn't so bad after all. The tube of glue's rather fun. Try to mend broken crayon sticks with it. Mend various other things about the room with it.

2.30 Go into hall to see if there's anything there I can mend with it. See Uncle George's hat hanging next to Ethel's. Think how funny it is that men's hats never have any trimming on. Wonder what they'd look like with trimming? Take Uncle George's into drawing-room and stick little white labels from the box he gave me all round it in a sort of ring.

Put it back on the hook to see what it looks like hanging up. Looks rather jolly. Will leave it hanging up for a bit, but must remember to take it down and take the labels off before Uncle George gets up from his nap.

2.45 Play with plasticine. Cover hair with it to see what I'd look like bald. Find I'd look jolly funny. Try to take it off, but it won't come. Play with rest of Uncle George's box. Make pattern on back of chair with drawing pins. Looks jolly nice.

3.0 Think it's about time people got up. Put on mask and open Ethel's door and pounce in on her to wake her up. She seems to think it's a jolly good joke and screams with laughter, then they all come running with smelling salts and things and it turns out that she's in something called hysterics, and they all go on at me and say it might have turned her brain.

3.30 Robert comes down. Sits on the chair I'd been mending things on with glue and gets stuck there. Makes an awful fuss about it. Gets unstuck after a long time and goes to the chair I'd been decorating with drawing pins and sits on a pin that I'd accidentally left point up. Makes another awful fuss.

I look jolly funny.

3.40 Father comes down. Goes into morning-room with detective novel. Uncle George comes down and makes an awful fuss about his hat that I'd forgotten to untrim. Goes on as if he'd been the King and I'd spoilt his diamond crown. It's only a rotten old hat, anyway, and it was him what gave me the labels so he oughtn't to grumble. Feel fed up with the box anyway, so throw rubber rings into fire. They aren't any good as catapults, anyway, because I've tried them and that's the only thing anyone could use them for.

3.45 Aunt Jane and Mother and Ethel come down. Start making an awful fuss about a few spills of glue on the carpet, and another fuss about the chair I'd decorated.

4.5 Very queer smell in the room. Another fuss about that. They say it's the rubber rings. I don't see how it possibly could be, but get tired of arguing with them. They all go into the morning-room, so I go with them. Father takes detective novel into dining-room. They start on me about plasticine in my hair.

4.10–4.15 Everyone very cross and dull. Try to cheer them up by throwing a few squibs into fire, but people don't seem to *want* to be jolly. All go into tea. Try ink spill and jam spill, but no one takes any notice. Have a jolly good tea, but no one else seems to eat much.

5.15 Everyone goes out for walk. Go out, too, and meet Ginger. Ginger says he's had a rotten Christmas. Everyone in his house as cross as what they are in mine. He's had an explosion with his chemicals with mixing the wrong things together. It broke a vase and gave his grandmother a headache, and they've taken it away from him. Meet Henry. Henry's had all his Christmas presents taken away from him – a saxophone, a box of fireworks, an air gun, a water pistol and a box of carpentering tools.

6.30 Come home again. Find card table put out. Offer to play Snap or Happy Families with anyone what would like to play. No one would like to. Say they're going to play bridge. Offer to play bridge with them. They say thank you, but they're hardly good enough to play with a brilliant player like me. Think they're being sarcastic. Ask what there is for me to do if they're all going to play bridge. They tell me to play quietly with my presents. I get out the penknife which is the only present I've not played with. See a fly on the card table and make a jab at it with penknife. Miss fly but find I've cut a hole in the green stuff that covers the table. It must be a jolly good penknife. They've not come to play yet, so get my glue quickly and try to mend it. Seems to make it worse. Decide to go out for long walk to give them time to find it and then forget about it.

7.30–8.0 Come home from long walk. They've found it but not forgotten about it. Everything very dull. Look for crayons, plasticine and glue but couldn't find them. Make a remark about it being stealing to pinch other people's things, but no one takes any notice. Read 'A Redskin's Revenge'. Jolly fine book. Wish I was a Redskin.

8.15 Supper. Everyone very dull and disagreeable. Ethel says I've ruined her nerves, and Uncle George says I've ruined his hat and Robert says I've ruined his trousers and Mother says I've ruined the drawing-room carpet not to speak of the chair and my bedroom wall.

8.30 Go to bed. Decide that it's been a rotten Christmas. Remember that I've never tried the camera trick or plate-lifter, but don't think they would have made much difference. Must try really hard to make things jollier next Christmas.

William's Christmas Presents

Christmas Eve. 2.30 p.m.

I've just come up to my room to think out quietly what
presents I'm goin' to give people to-morrow. P'r'aps you'll think
I've left it rather late, but then I've been very busy lately an'
haven't had time to think out anything.

Me an' Ginger an' Douglas an' Henry have found an empty
house, an' we've been goin' there every day an' makin' fires an'
havin' a fine time an' nobody's found us out yet. But I'll tell
you all about that another time.

At present, I'm tryin' to think out my Christmas presents.
I'm goin' to give people presents that don't cost any money,
partly because people say that it's not the money that matters,
but the thought, and partly because I haven't got any money.

25

Now, I'm goin' to start thinkin' deep this minute. I'm sittin' in front of the lookin' glass so that I can see myself thinkin'. I've got a face like the faces people have on in the pictures when they're thinkin' deep.

I bet I'd make a jolly good picture actor. I've a jolly good mind to be one when I grow up. Only I'm not going to be the sort that gets pushed down precipices an' things – I'm going to be the sort that pushes other people.

But to return to my thinkin' deep. I've got to think of something for my mother first.

Wait a minute.

I'm thinkin' very deep.

I've got it.

3.0 p.m.

I've just finished makin' the present for my mother. I bet you're wantin' to know what I've made her, so I'll tell you. I've made her two tea-cosies.

I remembered she'd said she wanted a new tea-cosy so I thought I'd make her one. I thought terribly deep about what to make it out of. I wish you'd seen me. I looked fine in the lookin' glass. I've quite decided to be an actor on the pictures when I grow up, an' suddenly I thought of the drawing-room cushions.

A tea-cosy, when you come to think of it, is only a cushion cut in two with a hole up the middle, so I thought that I'd make two tea-cosies out of a cushion. I thought that there are ever so many too many cushions in the drawing-room. F'rinstance, there needn't be three cushions on the sofa. Two would be quite enough.

So I slipped downstairs an' got one of the cushions off the sofa and luckily no one saw me.

I don't mean by this that I think I was doin' anythin' wrong, takin' the cushion to make two tea-cosies, because I knew that I was doin' a deed of kindness an' a deed of kindness can never be wrong – but my family can't understand that sometimes.

Well, it was far more difficult than you'd think to make
those tea-cosies. I don't suppose
you've any idea what messy
stuff there is inside cushions.
It gets everywhere, and sort of
clings to you. I can't think why
people put stuff like that inside
them.

You haven't
any idea what
messy stuff there is
inside cushions.
It gets everywhere and
sort of clings to you.

Anyway, I did my best, and, as grown-up people say, one can't
do more. I cut it in two an' sort of made two holes up in the
messy stuff by pressin' it with my hands. I took a lot of trouble
over them an' she ought to be very grateful to me.

She'll have to be very careful how she uses them, of course. I
mean, she'll not have to hold them upside down much, because
the messy stuff comes out so, however much you press it down
with your hands, an' she'll have to be very careful how she puts
it on an' off the tea-pot or the messy stuff'll fall on to the tea-pot.
But they ought to be all right, if she's careful. An' they look very
pretty, all made of silk an' embroidered in beautiful colours.

Now, I'm beginnin' thinkin' deep about my father's present.
I'm gettin' that face better an' better. I think I won't wait till
I'm grown-up to start actin' for the pictures. I'll try 'n' find a
play what has a boy in it thinkin' deep an' I'll start at once.
This face I've got on now'd look fine in a picture.

I'm thinkin' very deep indeed.

I've got it.

3.30 p.m.

I've just finished makin' my
father's present. I'll tell you all
about it. After thinkin' very
deep indeed for some minutes
(I wish you could have seen my
faces) I suddenly got an idea. My
father's nearly always smokin' a
pipe, so I thought I'd take him a
pipe for his Christmas present.

Now, a pipe's made of wood
an' it's quite an easy sort of
shape – jus' straight along an'
then up – so I thought I'd make
him a pipe. I went down to get a
piece of wood from the firewood
place. I found a nice fat piece.
Then I remembered I'd lost my
penknife. I'd lost it in the wood
when me an' Ginger an' Henry
an' Douglas were playing Red Injuns there.

It's a good deal harder
to carve a pipe out of
piece of wood than you'd think.

So I thought deep again for a few minutes an' then I got
another idea (I find that if I think deep enough I always get
another idea) an' the idea was that surely if I was makin' a
present for him he wouldn't mind me usin' his razor to make
it with.

So I fetched his razor (fortunately, no one saw me. Again, I
don't mean that I think I was doin' wrong, because, as I said
before, a deed of kindness can never be wrong, but sometimes

people meetin' you act hastily without stoppin' to consider whether you're doin' a deed of kindness or not, so I was glad no one met me), an' started carvin' his pipe from the piece of wood.

Now, I won't pretend that I made it look exactly like the sort of pipe you see in shops, because I didn't. It's a good deal harder to carve a pipe out of a piece of wood than you'd think, an' I've now got a greater respect for pipe shop people than what I had before I started.

But I did the best I could (which, as I said before, is all we can do, an' ought to please people).

It did go straight along an' then up same as a pipe does, but I won't pretend that it turned out quite the same as a pipe in a shop. Of course, the next thing was to get it brown, same as a pipe in a shop, an' that needed a lot more deep thinkin', because I hadn't any brown paint an' I hadn't any money to buy any, but after the deep thinkin' I suddenly remembered that the cough mixture in the medicine cupboard is a very beautiful brown.

So I fetched it an' poured it out into my wash-basin an' gave the pipe a good washin' in it. It did make it a bit brown, though not so brown as I'd hoped it would. However, I find more an' more as life goes on that one seldom does get anything just as one hopes, an' that it's no use worryin'. So I poured the cough mixture back into the bottle an' put it into the medicine cupboard again an' put the pipe to dry.

Then suddenly I remembered that I'd forgotten to make the little hole they breathe the smoke through. I tried makin' it with the razor, but the razor didn't seem to be actin' now as well as it had done at first, an', anyhow, it would be very hard to make the little hole right through with a razor, even if it had been doing.

But I didn't worry. I told myself that my father could easily make that little hole himself or take it to a pipe shop to be done. If I'd made all the rest of it surely he could do a little thing like that, just to help finish it off.

The next ones to think of are Ethel an' Robert, but it's teatime, an' as you can imagine, I'm pretty well wore out with all that deep thinkin' so I'm goin' down to tea.

4.45 p.m.

It's a jolly good thing I went down to tea. I don't mean because of the jelly an' cream cakes, though those were jolly good an' a nice surprise, because I didn't know they were goin' to start good food till tomorrow, but it was a good thing, because I listened to Robert an' Ethel talkin', an' I found out by that what they'd like for Christmas. I didn't talk much myself because of the jelly an' cream cakes, an' so it gave me a good chance of listenin' to others. Robert was talkin' about fishin' an' arrangin' all about a fishin' holiday he's goin' to have next summer. Now, with Robert bein' grown up, I somehow never thought of him bein' fond of fishes. It seems hard to believe he is, because often he's seen me goin' off to catch minnows in the stream with a jar an' a net an' never seemed to want to come with me.

However, to hear him talk he certainly seemed fond of them, so that's what I'll give him for his Christmas present. I'll give him some of my minnows. I've got a good many more than I want, anyway, so it'll be quite a nice present to give him.

I'll wash early to-morrow mornin' an' then put some of them into my washbasin outside his bed-room door an' it will be a nice surprise for him when he comes out.

And, with listenin' very carefully while I was eatin' the jelly and cream cakes, I found out what Ethel likes, too, an' I'm goin' to make it for her now.

5.30 p.m.

I've finished makin' Ethel's present. I bet you're longin' to know what it is. Well, she was talkin' at tea about a beautiful present what a friend of hers had had given her for Christmas. I was listening very carefully to everything she said, because I wasn't talkin' much myself because of the jelly an' cream cakes. She said it was a hand-made leather box an' how beautiful they were an' how expensive. So I thought I'd make her a hand-made leather box.

I'd got a box I'd used for keepin' caterpillars in in the caterpillar season. It had a few air holes in, of course, but they wouldn't show when I'd covered it with leather. It was very fortunate I had some glue. I'd had it given me some weeks ago an' my mother had taken it off me the first day because somehow or other it got on her things and she'd only given it back to me yesterday.

She'd probably given it back to me because of the kind feelings to everyone that Christmas is supposed to bring (not that one ever notices this much) an' p'r'aps, too, because she thought I mightn't have given her a present if she went sticking on to my glue. I must say she'd have felt a bit ashamed to-morrow when she found those lovely silk tea-cosies if she hadn't given it me back.

Well, I'd got the box an' the glue an' the only thing to find now was the leather. I had to think very deep about that till suddenly I remembered my Sunday gloves which are made of leather. I hesitated a minute, but I remembered that we are supposed to make a sacrifice in order to give pleasure to other people, so I decided to sacrifice my Sunday gloves to give Ethel pleasure. I got the scissors an' began cutting them out.

All I can say about hand-made leather boxes is that they're not half as beautiful as what Ethel made out. I cert'nly managed to cover all of it with leather, except a bit here an' there, but it looked rather funny an' the lid wouldn't go on. I tried makin' one of the fingers into a handle, which was a very good idea, but didn't turn out exactly as I meant it to. Anyway, Ethel must like hand-made leather boxes or she wouldn't have talked like that at tea. So it'll be all right as far as Ethel's concerned.

There's still Aunt Jane an' Uncle Frederick who are stayin' with us, but I'm gettin' really wore out with all this hard work an' deep thinkin'.

6.0 p.m.

I've arranged presents for Aunt Jane an' Uncle Frederick. Aunt Jane's always talkin' about her cat what she loves so dearly, so I'll give her one of my mice for it. I've got far too many, anyway. It's time something happened to some of them. I'll put it in a box an' put it outside her bed-room door. An' I'll give Uncle Frederick a bottle of liquorice water. It's jolly good stuff, an' I've got a lot of it I made yesterday, an' haven't drunk yet. I'll go to the medicine cupboard again an' find a little empty bottle to pour some into.

Christmas Day

You'd have thought they'd all have liked those presents I gave them, wouldn't you?

Well, they didn't. And it wasn't my fault. I took enough trouble over them, didn't I?

How was I to know that my mother would be mad at havin' two beautiful silk tea-cosies given her?

How was I to know that my father would make such a fuss over his old razor?

How was I to know that Robert would fall over that bowl of fish an' tumble downstairs?

How was I to know that Ethel didn't really like hand-made leather boxes, spite of sayin' she did, an' that she'd get glue all over her dress, an' that they'd all be so mad at me for sacrificing my Sunday gloves?

It will jolly well serve them right if I don't give them *any* presents next Christmas!

How was I to know that Aunt Jane would get her finger bit by the mouse, an' scream like that?

How was I to know that Uncle Frederick wouldn't know it was liquorice water, but would think it was hair restorer, same as it said on the label of the empty bottle I found, an' rub it all into his hair before he came down?

Well, all I can say is that it will jolly well serve them right if I don't give them *any* presents next Christmas!

Commonsense about Holidays

Of all the things in the world what want reformin I think that holidays want it most. I don't mean that there is anything wrong with having holidays but what I say is that there's far too few of them.

It seems to me very cruel that poor children should be expected to struggle through twelve or thirteen weeks' hard work completely wearin out their brains jus for three or four miserable weeks holiday. I do not mean by this that I think holidays are in any way miserable in themselves. It is the meanness of givin us so few that is miserable.

It often seems funny to me that the noble and kindhearted people what make up societies for doing good to other people what don't really need any good doing to them, such as savages what must lead immensely happy lives fighting and dancing war dances till people come along reformin them and making them miserable – what I mean to say is that it's funny to me that these noble and kindhearted people make such a fuss about reformin savages and people what don't need it and do nothin at all about us poor boys what do.

I cannot help thinking that such people are less noble and kindhearted than they try to make out. There are of course societies for helping children one way and another such as not lettin them go into public houses which look rather jolly to me – all lit up and with people singing and dancin and having fun in them – but it's very funny that there's no society to stop poor children bein forced to use their brains for thirteen weeks without stoppin till they're completely wore out and then only givin a few miserable weeks to rest them.

The natral result is that we go back to school with our brains still in a state of being wore out so we get awful reports and our fathers get mad and many unpleasant things happen to us while if only they'd arrange it the other way round so's we could have the twelve or thirteen weeks to rest our brains in and the holiday time to use them in they'd find our brains nice and fresh and rested and everything would be better for all concerned especially us. A still better idea would be to keep the brain *always* completely rested so as to have it always nice and fresh.

Speaking for myself my brain often feels completely wore out after only one day's work especially if its Latin or Geometry. I think that mine's a special sort of delicate brain that needs an extra lot of rest like the people with weak backs and weak chests what have to take special care of them. No one but myself seems to understand this. I once tried to explain it to my father but all he would say was that I could rest it if I liked by staying away from school the next day, but I must stop in bed and have only bread and water because that was specially good for the brain.

Mine is the sort of brain that rests best if my body is climbing trees or playing Red Indians and eating a lot. I think that a lot of my food must go to my brain because I am nearly always hungry. But my father is the sort of father that its simply no use explaining things to.

Occasionally when my brain feels really wore out I give it a day's holiday myself because I think we all have a duty to our brains not to let them get quite wore out so I let my brain have a complete rest and my body goes climbing trees in the wood and bein a Red Indian and such like.

I think that we all ought to take the greatest care of our brains in childhood because when we are grown up we may want to use them in some emergency and it would be very disappointing to find them all wore out – which I think is what often happens to grown ups. I try to take great care of mine by not usin it too much. In our village there was an old woman what had never been to school and couldn't write or read but when she died they found hundreds an hundreds of pounds hid in a stocking under her floor which was very clever of her and a proof of what I've been saying.

After all probly famous people like Robinson Crusoe an Guy Fawkes an Romulus an Remus (who were brought up by wild animals which must have been great fun) did not have to use their brains much in childhood, and that is the reason why they turned out great men and we read their names in our history books. But the way I have to keep on continually using my brain day after day and week after week with no rest at all I don't suppose that anyone will ever read my name in any history book except the one I am using now at school and in which I have written my name twice on nearly every page. I have also written

> 'Black is the raven; blacker the rook,
> Blackest is he who steals this book.'

I've written that on nearly every page, too (because one must do something in prep. and it's the dullest history book you ever saw all about Parliament an' suchlike). I didn't make it up of course. Another boy told me it. And all over the beginning and end pages I've wrote,

> 'Steal not this book for fear of shame,
> For here goes all the owners name.'

And then I've wrote my name. I didn't make that up either. It was made up by some poet or other, I don't know who. I've written it twenty times in the back and twenty times in the front which is rather clever. Ginger could only get it in fifteen times.

On the page where the name of the book is I've wrote my name forty times and my address endin with 'England, Western Hemisphere, the World, the Universe'. So I should think there's not much danger of me losing that book. Not that I'd care if I did except they would probly make me buy another and I'd be sorry to lose that picture of Queen Elizabeth what I've put spectacles and a moustach and a red nose on to because it looks awfully funny and I mightn't be able to do it so nice again. I've done that to all the pictures in the book and some of them look awfully funny.

The first thing I should do if the government asked me to start reformin the holidays would be simply to make the term time the holidays and the holidays the term time and then everything would be much nicer. I think that the only people who would

I should make every other year a complete holiday. I am quite sure the school-masters won't mind.

not like it would be our mothers who have a strange dislike to havin us at home for longer than three or four weeks at a time but I think that they ought to make an effort to conquer this feelin. After all we do a lot for them in the way of brushing our hair and washing our hands when we don't want to and when we know that it's quite unnecessary so I think that they might do just that little thing for us. Then I should make every other year a complete holiday so as to save all this terrible wearin out of our brains an make us have a little left for when we grow up.

I am quite sure that the school-masters won't mind. I cannot imagine anyone who isn't a loony likin teachin me and Ginger and Douglas and Henry. I suppose that they're not clever or brave enough to do anything else, or in some cases I think its people so full of meanness and cruelty that they've got to let it out or bust and so they turn schoolmasters. I'm not going to be a schoomaster when I grow up, though I shuln't mind being a master if the masters in our school could be turned into boys. I often think what fun that would be.

Then comes the question of going away for holidays to seaside places and suchlike. Persnally I don't like seaside places. They are too much in the town. At least all the ones I've been to are. One is expected to be continually washing ones hands and brushing ones hair and changing ones collar which would spoil any holiday. It's  always been a mystry to me why people are expected to be cleaner in the town than what they are in the country. One of the reasons why I am so fond of the country is that one is not expected to be specially clean in it. I've never been able to see what people see in streets and shops. My mother an grown up sister can spend hours jus lookin in to shop windows at clothes an suchlike which is a mystry to me.

I do not mean that I dislike the sea but how one can be expected to enjoy it without gettin ones clothes wet is also a

How one can be expected to enjoy the sea without gettin ones clothes wet is a mystry to me.

mystry to me. The rocks and seaweed at the seaside are quite interesting. I read in a book once that seaweed was edible so I looked up edible in the dictionary and it said eatable so I et some jus to see if it was and I was very sick and nearly died. The doctor said that it was a slight billious attack and that I didn't nearly die but you can natrally tell yourself when you're nearly dyin better than other people. Its a feelin that you can't possbly

make any mistake about. I have had it several times so I know it. I expect the catch in it was that everythings eatable unless its a great huge thing like a hippopotamus but that doesn't say it won't make you very sick and nearly die. I expect the

man in that book was jus pullin people's legs. I expect he's had ever so many people sick and nearly dyin with it.

I'd always rather spend my holidays at the country than at the seaside and I'd rather spend them in the country near my

home than in strange country, because in the country near my
own home I know the best places for fishin and gettin conkers
and playin Red Indians and where the best nests are (but I only
take one from each which they don't miss because they can't
count) and which farmers don't mind or can't run very fast and
which farmers get mad at the very sight of you for some reason
or other which has always been a complete mystry to me.

The more I think about holidays the more I wonder why
there is anything else in the world. I've never met anyone who
likes work so I don't see why we should have any. I think that
someone ought to make a law sayin that no one was to do any
work and that everyone should have holidays all the time. Coo,
that would be a jolly fine idea, wouldn't it?

New Year's Day

I think that New Year's Day is almost as wrong as Christmas an' I will try to tell you jus' what I think is wrong with it.

For one thing it comes too near Christmas Day. Everyone makes such a big effort to be good-tempered on Christmas Day that they are nat'rally bad tempered for weeks after. There is also the bitter feeling of those who have kissed the wrong person under the mistletoe or who have failed to kiss the right one which sometimes lasts for months.

I know pers'nally that the week after Christmas is a very bad time to ask anyone anything because it is so difficult to find anyone who is in a good temper. Fathers are always brooding on how much more it all cost than they had hoped it would – and that makes them almost inhuman so that at any little sound or a bit of holly on their chairs or a simple question from poor children who are merely trying to gain knowledge, they become quite frenzied.

Mothers are not much better.

They are all the time brooding on how much trouble it was, and what a lot everyone ate, and how Aunt Martha needn't have wanted a fire in her bedroom every night, and things like that. Christmas has an enraging effect on fathers but a bittering effect on mothers.

Fathers, as I have said, work it off in frenzied outbursts, but mothers work it off in cold meat and bread-and-butter pudding and saying that no, you mayn't have those boys in again – look at all the mess they made yesterday – and will you or will you not keep that dog out of the kitchen and things like that.

Grown-up brothers and sisters are just as bad.

Brothers are less violent than fathers simply because they are a little younger and haven't yet attained their full powers of violence, but they are pretty bad. They pretend that they are mad because you have meddled with their motor cycle or made them an apple-pie bed or used their hair brushes to brush your dog, but really you know quite well that it is because they kissed the wrong person or failed to kiss the right one under the mistletoe on Christmas Day. And it is useless to try to help them in this because the right ones change so frequently.

Once, wishing to put my brother in a good temper, so that he might not mind when he found that his watch had stopped (though I'd put back the parts exactly as I took them out) I went to a good deal of trouble to get him under the mistletoe with a girl with whom he had been passionately in love – only to find that he had been out of love with her for nearly a week and had almost forgotten what she looked like.

It turned out, too, that through my doing that he had missed a chance of getting under the mistletoe with the new girl. I do not wish to draw out this incident to too great a length, so will merely add that he was most inhuman about the watch.

Sisters are just the same, of course, except that their right people change even more frequently, and they are even worse tempered. They always pretend in public to be very sweet-tempered and always get most enraged when you let on that they are not.

New Year comes along before people have got over those feelings of rage and bitterness that Christmas always leaves behind it. I do not wish to harp upon my own personal feelings, but how can any human being be expected to form good resolutions of love and kindness to all the world when his heart is still full of the feelings caused by Aunt Martha and Uncle John who gave him a book of poetry and half-a-dozen handkerchiefs for his Christmas present?

I once heard someone say that human nature, though beautiful, has its limitations, and that is a sentiment I quite agree with.

My own nature, though beautiful, has its limitations.

It could not possibly love Aunt Martha or Uncle John only a week after Christmas. It takes more than a week for memories of poetry and handkerchiefs to die in any human breast.

This is why New Year resolutions are always a failure. You are supposed to make good resolutions to be kind and loving when you are only just forming plans of vengeance on the people who have insulted you at Christmas with silly presents of poetry and handkerchiefs, etc. If New Year's Day came – say – two months later you would then have successfully carried out your plans of vengeance and would be ready to be kind and loving to all the world. It is ridiculous to ask a poor boy to be kind and loving to all the

A book of poetry for a Christmas present!

world before he has done anything about the inhuman presents given him by unfeeling relations or the various insults laid upon him by his grown-up brother and sister.

The idea is, of course, a very good one for the unfeeling relations and the brother and sister, but not for the poor boy. It is quite clear to me that New Year's Day was put where it is by someone who hoped it would take people's minds off the things he'd given them on Christmas Day.

Then another point is the *sort* of good resolution you are expected to make. You are not allowed to choose your own good resolution.

For instance, I am quite ready to make resolutions to be cheerful because we read in the Bible that cheerfulness is a Christian virtue, but the more cheerful I try to be – singing an' playin' musical instruments an' things like that – the madder people seem to get.

We read a lot in poetry about the hearts of parents bein' gladdened by the sound of children's feet an' voices about the house, but the sound of my feet an' voice about the house does not seem to gladden my parents' hearts, and indeed I have

The more cheerful I try to be the madder people seem to get.

never come across any parents in real life with hearts like that. All the parents I know in real life instead of being gladdened tell you in an unfeeling fashion to stop making that infernal din or they'll come and make you. At least, fathers do. Mothers merely ask if you're *tryin'* to make their heads ache. I often think how much I'd like to have the sort of parents we read about in poetry.

But to return to New Year's Day an' good resolutions. As I said, cheerfulness, though distinctly mentioned in the Bible as a Christian virtue, is not allowed as a good resolution.

Helpfulness, too, which one would imagine would be welcomed as a good resolution, is not allowed. Personally, helpfulness is a virtue which I am very fond of. I like helping people. I like doing little things for my brother such as trying to mend his watch for a surprise for him or testing his new motor cycle for him, and things like that.

I like to help cook by seeing that her tarts and cakes are all right and eating up things left over from parties just to get them out the way for her.

I like to help my mother and sister and brother, too, in lots of little ways. But I have found out that helpfulness is a virtue that some people cannot appreciate and whenever I mention it as my good resolution people shudder and quickly say that I must not on any account be helpful.

There are a lot of strange things in the world, but I think that one of the strangest is that people should prefer a poor boy to be sad and unhelpful rather than cheerful and helpful, don't you?

Instead of those beautiful virtues I have just mentioned, I am told to have for my good resolutions punctuality and tidiness and good manners. Well, what I say is that the Ancient Britons were a fine, noble, heroic, manly race, and if they had no use for such things as these (and I cannot imagine a punctual tidy good mannered Ancient Briton) why should we? What I say is, who are we to set ourselves above a fine, noble, heroic, manly race like what the Ancient Britons were?

If my hair happens to have got a bit untidy . . .

The last thing I have to say about good resolutions is that grown-up people's idea of them is very one-sided. I have never yet observed any of them bein' different to me on New Year's Day from what they were on the day before.

If I start playing musical instruments on January 1st I am told to stop.

If I start singin' or playin' musical instruments on January 1st I am told to stop in jus' the same tone of voice as I was on December the 31st. If I happen to have overlooked a little dirt on my hands or if my hair happens to have got a bit untidy on January 1st, people say exactly the same things to me about it as they said on December 31st.

I am expected to behave quite different to everyone else but I cannot help noticin' that no one else behaves any different to me.

I'm sure that when you have read this you will agree with me that New Year's Day is all wrong, an' Ginger an' Douglas an' Henry an' me have decided to do something about it as soon as we're grown up, an' we hope that all of you what have read this will help us.

Home for the Holidays

Thursday, December 21st.

Breaking-up day. Old Whiskers, our form master, gave us a jaw, and told us to behave so well in the holidays that our families would be sorry instead of glad when they came to an end. I said that I thought it was very unkind to try to make people sorry instead of glad, but he told me to shut up, so I shut up though I could have said a lot more.

Had a look at my report in the cloakroom. Seemed pretty awful – all poors and weaks and unsatisfactorys and does not works and could do betters and things like that, just the sort of report I always seem to get, and that my father goes on making a fuss about for weeks, though I try to explain to him that they only put things like that because they're in a bad temper with end of term; but my father's a very unreasonable man and it's no good explaining things to him.

Clarence Medlow was looking at his report next to me in the cloakroom and he'd got a jolly good one, all goods and excellents and improvings and has worked wells and things like that. That's just because he enjoys sitting quiet and learning history dates and exports and imports and French verbs and how Horatius kept the bridge and things like that, and I don't.

I often try to explain to my family that it's simply that some people like sitting still and learning lessons and some people don't, and I'm one of the ones that don't, and it's not my fault and that if I enjoyed sitting still and learning lessons, I'd do it same as the other people do that enjoy it, but I don't, and so I can't, but they don't even try to understand.

Anyway, Clarence lives with an aunt who thinks he's wonderful whatever he does (I often wish my aunts were like that), so it doesn't really matter what his reports are like so I had a brainy idea and asked him to swop reports.

He asked me how much I'd give him and I said sixpence, which was all I'd got, and I was saving it up to buy presents for my family, not that they deserve any the way they go on at me over my reports.

Clarence's aunt gives him a lot of pocket money, but he spends it all on cream buns. He's nearly as fond of cream buns as what he is of fractions and imports and how Horatius kept the bridge, and that sort of thing.

Anyway, he said he'd swop reports for sixpence, and I gave him the sixpence, and we scratched out our names on the reports, and I wrote my name on his and his on mine, and tried to make my writing look like old Whisker's, though it didn't much, even when I'd finished. I made rather a lot of blots and things, too, but I told Clarence to tell his aunt that old Whiskers had sprained his hand and couldn't help writing like that.

I gave him the sixpence and he went straight across the road to the shop where they sell cream buns.

Then I went home with Ginger, and we went a long way round through the woods and had a game of scouting each other. Then I went home and gave my report to my mother, and instead of looking pleased, she began to look worried and said: 'Oh, William, have you been feeling quite well this term?' I said: 'Yes, it's jus' that I've started takin' an interest in sums and dates and imports and Horatius and stuff like that like what you've always wanted me to.'

Then Ethel, my sister, who's always poking her nose into things that aren't her business, said: 'Why have you written your own name on?' So I said: 'Old Whiskers has hurt his hand.'

Then Ethel said: 'Why is there another name scratched out underneath?' and I said that old Whiskers had made a mistake and had to scratch it out.

And jus' then Clarence's aunt came up in an awful bate, saying that I'd forced her little darling to give me his report,

'Why have you written your own name on this report?'

and she'd known at once it couldn't be Clarence's because it said poor for essay, and dear little Clarence's essay on the stars had almost made her cry, it was so beautiful, and Clarence's favourite occupation was mental arithmetic, and she knew that his report for arithmetic couldn't possibly be no improvement at all, very poor.

Of course, Clarence had made out that it was all my fault, so I went out very quietly while they were all arguing about it and went round to Clarence to see if I could get my sixpence back out of him, at any rate.

I found him sitting on their wall eating a cream bun. He said he was sorry, but he'd spent all the sixpence on cream buns, and I asked him to give me one, but he put the end piece in his mouth and said he was sorry, but that was the last bit.

So I knocked him off the wall and went for a long walk to give them time to get over it at home, and to think out a way of getting some more money to buy them Christmas presents, though I must say they don't deserve it the way they treat me.

Stayed out for nearly an hour, but they still hadn't got over it when I got back. They all said some very nasty things; my father especially, and wouldn't even give me any money to buy presents for themselves which is what I call cutting off their nose to spite their face, as people say.

Went out again after tea and met Ginger and Douglas and Henry. Found that none of them had any money to buy Christmas presents.

Ginger had had a lot of money, nearly ninepence, but he'd slipped through the greenhouse roof by mistake when he was practising climbing over it from one tree to another and had had his money took off him to pay for the new glass. Nobody seemed to mind that he hurt himself very badly, but only said serve you right in the cruel way of grown-ups.

Douglas hadn't had much money only threepence, and he'd met a boy that said if he'd give him all the money he'd got he'd give him something that was worth a guinea, which is a pound and a shilling, which is a jolly lot of money.

Douglas didn't believe him at first, but the boy said cross my throat and on my honour, and promised that the price of a guinea would be actually printed on this thing he was going to give Douglas. So Douglas gave him his threepence, and the boy gave him an old pill-box with worth a guinea a box printed on it and run away so fast that Douglas couldn't catch him.

Henry had nearly got sixpence because his godmother had promised him sixpence if he'd chop up an old clothes-horse for her for firewood, but quite by mistake and not meaning to at all, Henry had chopped up the new instead so though he'd taken a lot of trouble over it she wouldn't give him the sixpence, and what's more, he's afraid he isn't going to get a Christmas present from her either. She was very unreasonable and wouldn't even listen when Henry tried to explain. We talked a bit about how unfair grown-ups are and then we decided to have a good think that night in bed about how to get some money for Christmas presents.

Friday, December 22nd

Met Henry and Ginger and Douglas. We'd all meant to have a good think last night in bed, but we'd all fallen asleep before we'd had time to, and hadn't woken till nearly breakfast time this morning. We were just wondering whether it would be any good getting up a show (we've got up some jolly good shows), when the lady that lives next door-but-two from Ginger came along and said that the vicar's wife had made her buy four tickets for a whist drive that afternoon and as she was going away for Christmas she hadn't time to take them to anyone herself so would we take them, and see if our mothers would like to go.

She said there were some very nice prizes, so we said thank you very much, and as soon as she'd gone we thought we'd like to go ourselves, because the prizes would be a very nice help to our Christmas presents because we could either give them as Christmas presents or sell them and make a lot of money. Henry once met a boy that knew another boy that had a cousin that won a tea-cosy in a raffle for twopence and his mother bought it off him for half-a-crown.

Things like that never seem to happen to oneself somehow, but there's always a chance.

The only thing was that none of us knew how to play whist but Ginger said he knew a boy that knew and he'd go round to him and find out and then tell us.

So he did and he came back and told us. It seemed a silly sort of game, but quite easy. If the next person to you puts a diamond down you have to put one down, too, and so on, and you must always try to put down a higher card than anyone else.

It didn't sound half such a good game as Snap, but we thought we'd be sure to win the prizes with it being so easy. We didn't tell our mothers we were going of course, because they always make a fuss whatever we tell them we're going to do, but we made ourselves sort of clean and tidy and went to the village hall where the thing was. No one seemed pleased to see us and there weren't any other boys there.

The prizes were jolly decent, though, a clock and a bag and

a photograph frame and a vase, just the sort of things that grown-ups will buy off you, so we thought we'd try very hard to put high cards on and win the prizes.

Well, it started, and I've never met such a bad-tempered set of people in my life as the people at that whist drive. Even when we put high cards on they got mad at us, and, of course, with such a lot of different sorts of cards and all so much alike you naturally get them a bit mixed up sometimes and the fuss they made when we put on a heart instead of a diamond or a spade instead of a club which you naturally can't help doing sometimes, and which doesn't make any difference anyway – well, I've never heard anything like it.

And they kept saying I'd done something called revoked, but I told them I couldn't possibly have considering I didn't even know what it meant.

Then there was something called trumping that the boy hadn't told Ginger about, and we never really found out what it was even at the end. Old Ginger kept forgetting he was playing whist and shouting 'Snap!' whenever two cards came the same which made the people at his table as mad as mad.

I've never heard anything like the fuss they made.

Then they had refreshments, and they were jolly good refreshments and we'd have enjoyed that part if everyone round us hadn't been so rude talking about us all the time, and saying how badly we'd been playing which we jolly well hadn't and how much we were eating as if they wanted us to starve.

I was beginning to think we wouldn't get the prizes after all, but the next game I played jolly well and got nearly every single trick, and I was feeling almost sure we would get them when it turned out that that game was a game called misery, and that it counted that I'd got no tricks at all, and I thought they were a rotten set of cheats and nearly told them so. Well, in the end, we didn't get any of the prizes, and we'd wasted a whole afternoon on it so we went away feeling jolly sick.

It was too late to do anything else so we decided to try to keep awake a bit to-night to have a jolly good think how to get the money.

Saturday, December 23rd

Met Ginger and Douglas and Henry first thing after breakfast. It was a funny thing, but we'd all fallen asleep again before we'd had time to have a good think. Ginger had had awful dreams about an ace of spades chasing him all night. He said he was never going to another of those whist things as long as he lived, and it had even put him off decent games like Snap and Beggar My Neighbour. Anyway, we felt jolly chewed because it was the last day before Christmas for buying presents and we still hadn't got any money, or even any plans for getting some, which was rather funny as I'm generally rather good at plans.

Then Douglas said that his aunt had sent a message to see if he'd go into Hadley to do some shopping for her, so we thought that if we all went and did it jolly well, she'd p'raps give us a tip with it being Christmas and everyone supposed to be full of peace and good will and such like, which no one ever seems to be to me Christmas or no Christmas.

Still, we all went round and she gave Douglas the basket and the money and a list of things we'd got to buy, and then she gave us all a gingerbread, and said if we did it very nicely she'd give us each a little Christmas box.

I've never found out why people call it box, but it's just one of the cracked things grown-ups do. Anyway, we set off to walk to Hadley through the woods and had a game or two on the way as we'd got all morning to do the errands, and people always say it's better to do a thing slowly.

Then we went on to Hadley and when we got there, Douglas found that he'd lost the bit of paper with the errands on. At first we didn't know what to do then I said that we'd better just buy the sort of things that grown-up people generally buy in shops and chance it.

So we bought a pound of butter and a pound of sugar and a pound of tea and a loaf and a nice cake just in case she was thinking of asking us to tea. We thought that with luck they might be just the things she'd got down on her list.

Anyway, we let Douglas go in alone and we stayed outside just in case the things were wrong, and soon we heard her going on at Douglas in a very bad-tempered way, saying that he'd bought her all the wrong things and she wished she'd gone herself, and he was the stupidest boy she'd ever come across, and a lot of unkind things like that so we knew it wasn't any good waiting for a tip or even a bit of cake.

Well, we'd wasted all morning over that and there was only the afternoon left so we met early in the afternoon to have another good think, but thinking made us feel so sleepy that we thought we'd go and have a game in the woods, to give ourselves a rest before we started thinking again.

We took Jumble to have a game with us, and in the middle of it he started barking and making an awful fuss and we thought he'd found a rabbit but when we went to look we found he'd got hold of something that looked like a toy animal of Henry's little sister's that had got run over by the garden roller. It was about as big as a rabbit, but it was more like a kitten and yet in another way it was rather like a rat.

We picked it up to stop Jumble eating it, and took it to the old barn. Then Ginger thought we'd have a show with it and

We decided we'd take it back to the woods.

Douglas stayed to look after it, and we all went home to write notices of the show.

I made a jolly fine one. THE ONLY RAT-RABBIT-KITTEN IN THE WORLD. HERE FOR ONE DAY ONLY. ENTRANCE 2d.

Ginger had made a jolly fine one, too. MAGIC ANIMAL. GUESS WHAT IT IS.

Douglas had found some sweets that his mother had thrown away because they'd gone candied, so he put on his notice: WONDERFUL WILD ANIMAL SHOW. REFRESHMENTS FREE.

We stuck the notices on the old barn, and on the stile leading to the road and waited all afternoon, but no one came. The animal was turning out jolly wild, too, and bit Ginger and me, and scratched Douglas, and got so mad that in the end as nobody seemed to be coming to the show we decided we'd take it back to the woods.

We felt jolly fed up because there was only one evening left now, and we weren't likely to find a way of getting money in just one evening. Anyway, we were walking along the road with the show, Ginger carrying it, and it scratching and biting for all it was worth and all of us feeling jolly fed up because however rotten your family is to you, you feel jolly mean not having any Christmas presents for them on Christmas Day, even if it's all their own fault, when suddenly a lady came running out of a house.

She made an awful fuss, and kissed the show and kissed Ginger who was carrying it, and would have kissed me and Henry if we hadn't ducked. For a long time we didn't know what she was making all the fuss about and then it turned out that the show was a very valuable toy dog she'd lost, and that she'd offered a reward of a pound to anyone that brought it back.

So she gave us a pound and that meant five shillings each. We went down to Hadley and bought some jolly decent presents for our families and had enough left over to buy some bulls'-eyes and rock and sherbet for ourselves.

And we bought a ha'porth of fruit drops for Jumble because he'd found the show.

School Is a
Waste of Time!

Education is one of the things what I feel very strongly about because I think that at present it is all wrong. I don't mean that I don't want people to be educated, because everyone ought to want to be educated so as to become a fine and noble character when he grows up, but education as done at present does not do that.

You have only got to look at the grown-ups around you to see that it does not do that.

There is not a single grown-up around me that I would like to be like when I grow up. Such characters as Eagle Eye, the Redskin Chief, and Buffalo Bill, and the viking in 'Erling the Bold', and Dick Turpin, seem to me to be fine and noble characters, and I would like to be like them when I grow up, but they, I am sure, would not have been such fine and noble characters if they had been educated like what we are.

I'm sure that Dick Turpin would have been a less fine and noble character if he'd had to waste as much of his life as I've had to on such meaningless things as Algebra and Geometry and the exports and imports of places he'd never heard of before and never wanted to hear of again. I feel very, very strongly about Geometry. I've never yet been able to understand from anyone what's the use of Geometry.

When I ask the Maths master, he says that it helps people to argue, but in that case, it doesn't seem any use me learning it, because I never get a chance to argue. Whenever I start arguing, either at home or at school, someone sits on me or smacks my

55

head. It seems silly to go to all that trouble and expense to get
me taught Geometry so that I may be able to argue and then
act like that whenever I do start arguing.

Our fathers must know what a silly and useless thing
education is because they've had it done to themselves, so
they must know. My father says that education is a glorious
thing, and that it fills our minds with noble thoughts and gives
us noble occupations to fill our leisure hours with in later life,
but I cannot help noticing that when *he* has any leisure hours,
he does not sit down to solve a Geometry problem or translate
a chapter from Caesar. No – he plays billiards or reads the
newspaper.

It seems a pity for his parents to have gone to all the trouble
and expense of having him taught Geometry and Latin just
so that he may spend his leisure hours playing billiards and
reading the newspaper. I once tried to put this point of view
before him, but he did not let me get far enough with it to
make it quite plain to him. I do not want you to think that I
blame my father for playing billiards or reading the newspaper
instead of solving Geometry problems and translating Caesar in
his leisure hours. I should be deeply ashamed if my father spent
his leisure hours solving Geometry problems and translating
Caesar. I cannot imagine anyone except a loony doing it.

No, the point of what I am saying is that they'd be just as well
off if they hadn't wasted all the hours of their youth, in which
they might have been doing so much more interesting things,
on Algebra and Latin and stuff like that that isn't any use to
anyone and that everyone knows isn't any use to anyone.

I used to wonder why our
fathers make their children be
educated in the same way
they'd been educated themselves when they must know
how useless it is in later life
for filling the leisure hours or
anything else. But the conclu-
sion I have come to is that it is
partly from the natural desire

of people who have been done in some way to get a little of their own back by seeing other people done in the same way, and partly because they look on school as a place where we are out of their way.

You see, if they acknowledged that school was useless they'd have to have us at home all day and, for some reason that I've never been able to understand, they greatly dislike having us home all day.

No one could try to be more helpful in his home than I try to be in mine. Only the other day, when my mother was out, I tidied all the drawers of her bureau (I found some very interesting things and had great fun with some sticks of sealing wax) and mended the dining-room clock (I don't mean that I actually made it go, but I rearranged the works so that they took up much less room inside which I think was an improvement), and started repainting her bedroom door (I'd nearly all the old paint off when she came home, but I couldn't be expected to know that she hadn't wanted it repainting), and chopped up some old boxes for firewood, just for a pleasant surprise for her when she came home.

She said that it was a surprise all right, but not a pleasant one. She said a lot more than that. She said as well that the old boxes I'd chopped up were anteeks and very valuable. Anteek, she said, means very old, so you'd think they were about ready for firewood, wouldn't you?

But she was so annoyed that I didn't argue in spite of having been taught Geometry at great trouble and expense so as to be able to argue. It seems strange to me that though I am continually doing little helpful things like that when I am at home, my parents openly welcome the day when the holidays end and I have to go back to school. Which brings us back to education, which is the subject I'm writing about.

I think it would be best for me to go through each subject in turn which we learn at school, and tell you what I think is wrong with it. I have already said all that it is necessary to say about Algebra and Geometry. I will merely say now that if all Geometry does is to teach you how to argue, then it's useless to teach it to me, because firstly I can argue quite well without it, and secondly, no one ever lets me argue.

Latin is a subject which I feel so deeply about that it is difficult to say all that I feel about it. I feel first of all that it is ridiculous to expect us to waste our youth learning a language that there's nobody alive who speaks it.

I have a deep respect for the Romans (I like that tale about Romulus knocking Remus on the head for jumping over his wall), but I cannot see how it helps them or us to make us learn their language when they've all been dead for thousands of years. As a matter of fact, one would respect them more deeply if one did not know their language, because no one can very deeply respect people who used expressions like 'Hic haec hoc', and pronounced all their words quite different from how they spelt them. I have had for some time a suspicion that Latin is simply taught us as a way by which masters may get a little of their own back for any little thing we may happen to have annoyed them by.

Then comes French. At first sight, French seems more natural and reasonable than Latin because the French people have not all died off same as the Latin people have (and I don't wonder the Latin people have all died off, having to speak a language like that), and may possibly come to England and want to talk to us in their own language. But the weak point of all this is that the French we are taught in schools is not the language that people talk in France. I know this for a fact because once, when I had been learning French for a whole term at school, I met a French boy and could not understand a word he said. He certainly did not say a single word that I had been taught in school.

I told my father this, hoping that he would say that I need not learn any more French at school as it was turning out so useless, but he was not sympathetic about it and said that, of course, it was the same language that they talked in France, and that he'd learnt it himself and ought to know.

I could not help noticing, however, that on the day the French boy came to our house to tea my father did not come in to tea at all, so I gathered that he was not very anxious to make use of the French that he had learnt at school, and I could not help suspecting that he thought it possible that the French boy might not understand it. As I have said, the French boy and I did not understand a word each other said all the afternoon, but we got on all right. They evidently fight in France just the same way as we do over here.

History, of course, like most other subjects, varies with the master who teaches it. We once had a very nice history master who was short sighted and very deaf. He used to give lessons in English history which we found very interesting because we were able to have conker battles and swop stamps and cigarette cards and throw ink balls at each other, and all bring mice or tortoises or some sort of animals and have races with them. He didn't mind at all, because he couldn't see or hear much.

I often think that schools would be far happier places for all concerned if more masters were like him.

He didn't stay long, however, and after him came a teacher who had a new way of teaching history. He made us act it. In his first lesson he taught us about King John signing the Charter, and I was King John. Ginger wanted to be the Charter, but he wouldn't let him be.

The scene did not end exactly as it ends in the history books because the unruly barons became so unruly that I had to get up and smack their heads, and Douglas upset the ink and the scene ended in confusion.

But that way of teaching history seemed a very good one to me, and when he started on the War of the Roses, the next week we started acting that with me the head of one side and Ginger the head of the other. Several of the desks got broke and all the ink got spilt and Ginger got a black eye and I got a bust nose.

That was the most interesting history lesson I ever remember having, but he left soon after that and another one came who didn't believe in learning history by acting it and was very suspicious and unsympathetic – always suspecting me of throwing ink balls about, and very strong and ruthless with the cane. History became a very dull subject after that.

I will say nothing about music and drawing, which are unimportant subjects, and only fit for girls who are generally better than we are at them because of their brains being formed different.

After all this you will wonder what I think ought to be taught in schools in order to make boys into the fine and noble characters they ought to be.

I think that Nature Study is most important. Not enough time is given in schools to the study of nature. I think that any boy who wishes to go out and study nature should be allowed to do so. As things are, whenever I stay away from school for a day in order to study nature, I am treated in a most ruthless fashion the next morning.

I think that it is most important to study nature in every way we can, by climbing trees, bird-nesting (if you only take one egg from each), wading in streams, fishing in rivers and ponds, scouting each other in woods, getting conkers and exploring the country around your home.

I don't think that anything ought to be allowed to come in the way of this. What, after all, are angles and indefinite pronouns and equations compared with a fine study like the study of nature?

Then, again, we should be encouraged to study the habits of animals. When I am caught studying the habits of, say, a white rat or hedgehog in a History or Latin lesson, I am treated in a ruthless fashion when really I ought to be encouraged.

And there is one last thing. It is the duty of us all to prepare to defend our country when an enemy lands upon its shores, so fighting and shooting should be two of the most important things in education. I think that fighting should be encouraged far more than it is. All the noble and heroic men in the past were good fighters.

We should try to fit ourselves to defend our country against enemies by keeping ourselves well practised in fighting. It is far more useful than Geometry and Latin. Where should we all be now if Nelson had spent his time doing sums and Latin unseens instead of fighting the battle of Waterloo?

Yet, whenever I try to keep myself well practised in fighting in order to be able to protect my country when an enemy lands upon her shores it is treated as a crime. When an enemy lands upon our shores what use is it to us to know that two sides of a triangle are together less than the third, or what particular battle Henry the Fifth conquered Napoleon in?

It would serve our masters and mothers right if when an enemy landed upon our shores we all sat down to solve problems and write out French verbs instead of fighting. As far as I am concerned, however, I am not likely to do this. I would rather fight any day. But I do think that fighting and good shooting ought to be more encouraged than what they are. I practise good shooting with a pea-shooter and a catapult, and a bow and arrows, but those around me are not grateful to me for thus fitting myself to defend them in time of need.

What after all is a few windows or greenhouse panes or even Miss Jones' cat (which I only hit its tail, whatever she says), in comparison with me making myself a good shot so as to be able to defend my country when enemies land upon her shores?

If I were at the head of education I should forbid anyone to teach Algebra or Geometry or Latin or French or anything like that, and I should have anyone that did it put in prison or treated in the ruthless way they treat other people, and the boys should give all their time to studying nature in their own way and learning to fight and shoot – also in their own way.

I sometimes think that when I'm grown up I'll be a school-master just so that I can educate boys the way I think they ought to be educated. It might be rather dull, however, so I'll probably stick to being a robber or a pirate after all.

The Job I'd Like Best

We are all told by our teachers and parents that we ought to be preparing ourselves to be great men when we grow up and this of course is true because we all want to be great men so that the world rings with our name and all men tremble at the sight of us. We cannot however all turn out to be this sort of great men because if we did there'd be no ordinary people left to ring with our name or to tremble at the sight of us, so some of us must make up our minds to be less famous than this and there are some unfamous careers which are very interesting indeed.

When we were young we generally wanted to be Red Indians or pirates and it is only as one grows older that one realises that there are no pirates left out of story books and that it is not possible to be a Red Indian except by birth which is impossible.

I think that it is a great pity that people have let pirates die out. Pirates are a noble and glorious career and one that I would have like to join if only people hadn't let them die out. With all these unemployed what we hear our fathers reading about at breakfast out of the newspapers you'd think that people wouldn't have let a noble and heroic career like pirates die out.

It is not even as if anyone would have to pay them because pirates do not need paying. They get money for themselves. I know that I myself personally would like very much to be a pirate. I have often practised being a pirate and think that I would make a very good one. Sometimes I think that when I am grown up I will set up as a pirate and start the career of pirate going again.

But leaving pirates there are still a great many noble and heroic careers left such as lion tamer and engine driver. I myself personally would like to be a lion tamer and have often practised being one getting some of my friends such as Ginger and Douglas to be the lions and I think that it is a career that I would thoroughly enjoy, but as I do not know any lion tamers personally it might be hard to get a job just at first. But, though I pass on to other careers, I have not altogether lost hope of being a lion tamer.

An engine driver would be great fun spinning through the air at a great rate and getting all over coal. But the great drawback to the career of an engine driver is that you've got to start out at the proper time and get back at the proper time and keep your engine clean which though fun at first might

It would be great fun, being an engine driver and getting all over coal!

become monotonous. I had once a great friend who was an engine driver who I got to know one summer holidays and he said that it was not a career that he would advise me to take up because it was not such fun as it looked. He said that though it might be fun getting all over coal it meant an awful lot of washing because people made you wash it off when you got home and the thought of that rather turned me against it because people seem to expect an awful lot of washing from one even now which I suppose would be ten times worse if one was an engine driver.

It would of course be nice to be famous and one can always become famous by discovering something like the man what became famous by discovering that apples fall to the ground. Its always been a mystery to me why people make such a fuss about him because you'd have thought that if they'd used their eyes they'd have seen for themselves that apples fall to the ground. It seems to me that it must have been much easier to become famous in those days than it is now. Or one might invent something but the great drawback to that is that everything has already been invented. My father says that I could win the gratitude of the whole world by inventing a silent boy but I think that he was being sarcastic.

When I was a good deal younger than I am now I used to think that I would like to go to sea. It sounded very fine and noble in all the books I read about it in and when my parents were harsh as they so often are I would make up my mind to run away to sea but generally the thought that the admiral might not let me have my dog along with me stopped me but it was not till I crossed over to Ireland by sea one summer to visit relations that I really gave up the idea. I learnt then that the sea in real life is not at all like the sea in books. There are certain things about the sea that are never mentioned in books about it and that made me decide not to be a sailor. I shall never forget what I suffered then and the thought of suffering like that all one's life as sailors must is a very terrible one to me.

There is also the career of being a soldier but then one might be a soldier all one's life and never be in a war which would be terrible while if there was a war on one could always give

There are certain things about
the sea that made me decide
not to be a sailor.

up one's ordinary career whatever it was such as lion tamer or
engine driver or discoverer and be a soldier till the war was over.
It must be terrible to waste one's life being a soldier without
any enemy to fight which is what some poor soldiers have to
do all their lives just walking about the streets talking to girls
and never being able to fight anyone. I know because I've seen
them doing it.

One career that I often think I would like to take up is that
of a sweet shop. I have often thought how nice it would be to
have a sweet shop. Though of course it would not be as exciting
as being a lion tamer or a pirate still I cannot imagine anything
more enjoyable. Sometimes I stand outside a sweet shop window
with its boxes and jars full of hundreds and thousands of sweets
and I imagine what I would feel like if I was the man it all
belonged to, and I know that I cannot imagine anything more
enjoyable.

If only I was the one it all belonged to!

At times like this I cannot imagine anyone ever wanting to be anything but a sweet shop man. It is dreadful to think of my father going up to town day after day to an office when he might be having a sweet shop. I cannot understand it. I myself personally would very much like to have a sweet shop. My father says that people who have sweet shops do not as a rule care for sweets but I am sure that he is wrong because it sounds to me quite impossible.

There are of course many other careers which one might take up as for instance doctors. It would be great fun to give medicine to people especially to the people one does not like. I cannot imagine anything being greater fun than that. I would very much like to be the doctor to some of the masters at my school and give them the sort of medicine our doctor gave me last week when I said I was too ill to go to school. (I went to school in the end because school, though unpleasant, was less unpleasant than the medicine). I would very much like to be doctor to our doctor. I bet I would give him some nasty stuff.

It must be fun in many ways to be a doctor. They are allowed to have skeletons which must be useful for playing tricks on people and giving them frights. But the great drawback to the career of doctors is that they have to pass exams and this is a terrible strain on the brain. I would not like that at all. Besides the terrible strain on the brain it leaves so little time for other and more interesting things.

Sometimes I think that I should like to write books. In fact I have already written several tales which were very exciting indeed about bill the reckless and the redfaces and things like that. Sometimes too I write the sort of tales about beauteous girls being captured by villains and heroes arriving in the nick of time. These are very exciting especially when the hero hears her calling help help and comes along and has a good fight with the villain and grinds him in the dust. I always like that part. I once wrote a play too and we acted it. At least we were going to but they said they could not read my writing so it ended in a fight which perhaps was more fun than the play would have been though it was a jolly good play.

The career of Member of Parliament too must be great fun in many ways. They haven't anything to do but make speeches and they needn't even make speeches if they don't feel like it and they're paid money whether they make speeches or not, which seems very nice for the Member of Parliament. I think that I should make a very good Member of Parliament because I am very good at making speeches. I can make speeches on nearly everything. Before you can be a Member of Parliament you have to make up your mind which side you are on. There are three sides – Conservative, Liberal and Bolshevist and they are all the same in that they all want to make the world better than it is now but they are different in the ways they want to make it better. Conservatives want to make it better by keeping everything just the same as what it is now and Liberals want to make it better by making everything quite different from what it is now and Bolshevists want to make it better by killing everybody but themselves which at first sight seems the simplest way but which would really make the world very dull because there'd be no one left for them to quarrel with.

My father is a Conservative though anyone would think from the way he treats me sometimes that he was a Bolshevist. My brother is a Liberal but I think it is only swank. My sister is not anything at all because she is not old enough to vote yet and she hopes she never will be. I always think that it must be great fun in the house of parliament getting up and making speeches all day long. The man who makes the most speeches is called the Speaker. I bet I'd be him if I was there.

Even if for any reason one does not want to be a Member of Parliament there are still a lot of careers to choose from. A friend of my brother's is going to be a lawyer. You learn to be a lawyer by eating dinners in a temple. This sounds to me a very nice way of learning to be anything and I think that I should make a very good lawyer. I'm certainly very good at eating dinners and it must be great fun to eat them in a temple. Then when you have eaten enough dinners you go about sending people to prison which must be great fun. It's sort of like a policeman but higher, because a lawyer has an office to do it in and the policeman does it in the street.

In spite of the dinners I'd really rather be a policeman than a lawyer because it must be such fun to make people mad by stopping their motor cars by just sticking out your hand and to write it all down in a little book whenever anyone does anything wrong.

And the very best thing about being a policeman is that you can always get to the front in a crowd. It is very annoying to an ordinary person such as me when a horse falls down or someone has a fit to be right at the back of the crowd and not to be able to see anything. A policeman never has this to put up with because he is always allowed to go to the front of a crowd even if he arrives late. Then when there is any sort of a procession again a policeman is allowed to stand in the very front so that he can see everything and also has the fun of feeling that he is stopping the people behind him from seeing anything because policemen's clothes and boots are so big that policemen have to be very big men in order to fill them properly. They make themselves big by eating porridge and practising dumbells.

I often think too that it would be great fun to be a burglar. The only drawback to being a burglar is that you get put in prison by the lawyers and policemen and prisons are very dull monotonous places where they don't let you play games or eat sweets so that in the end the lawyers and policemen have the best of it especially as burglars have to be small because of getting through larder windows so that in a fight with policemen they generally get licked so that on the whole I'd rather be a policeman than a burglar because I think that they really have more fun.

But in spite of all this I still think that being a pirate must be the best fun of all and I'm certainly going to be that when I grow up.

My Summer Holiday

I think that the worst part of the summer holidays is that they're so long coming that you begin to think they're never going to come at all and then the minute they come they're over. I don't mean that I don't think they couldn't be nicer than what they are, because I do.

I think it would be nice to have snow and ice in summer sometimes as well as in winter, then when you fall through the ice you could just go and lie in the sun till you're dry instead of having to go home to bed. And you could go on having snowball fights after tea 'stead of having to come in cause its dark. It would be much more fun snowballing people in summer clothes than when they're wearin' thick overcoats and things.

Well, what I wanted to tell you about this summer holidays was about me going to stay with my aunt. I've got hundreds of aunts but this one had never seen me. Robert said that that was why she asked me, but I don't see any sense in that. Sometimes Robert says things that make you feel reelly sorry for his branes. Well I didn't want to go to stay with this aunt. I didn't know her but I've known enough aunts to know what she'd be like.

I think that all these relations are all wrong. The animals don't have them and I think we ought to try to live natchural like the animals. You'd never find a lion going to stay with its aunt. It's got aunts but it doesn't know them, and its as like as not to start fighting them when it meets them and thats the way I think we ought to be. Its more natchural. Well, I didn't want to go to this auntys. I said I wanted to live a more natchural life like the animals but its no use me talkin to people because no one ever listens to anything I say.

I found out afterwards that Robert and Ethel wanted me to go to stay with this aunt because they wanted to have a picnic while I was away. They've got a funny sort of idea that I spoil things when all I ever try to do at picnics and suchlike is to try and put a bit of life into them and make them jolly.

So we had a lot of arguments about me going to stay with this aunt. They said it would do me good to have a change of air and I told them that my body had got used to this air and a diffrent sort would give it a shock and might kill me, but they didn't seem to mind. I bet no one ever had such a funny family as mine. When I tell them that something they want me to do such as going to school when I'm feelin ill is as like as not to kill me they don't seem to mind a bit and yet when I want to do somethin that I *know'll* do me good like going out to fish in the stream when I've got a bit of a cold they carry on like anythin an won't let me. Seems as if they can't make up their minds whether they want me to die or not.

Well, I argued with my family about lions and not wantin them to be lonely but they wouldn't take any notice. They never do take any notice of anythin I say. Someday I may have somethin important to say an theyll miss it through not listenin and I hope it'll teach them a lesson.

But I'd made up my mind not to go an stay with this aunt and I'd made a plan of hiding in the summer house till it was too late for the train, but somethin happened that made me change my mind.

Ginger and me'd been playin in Genral Moult's garden while he was away. I never see anything wrong in playing in peoples gardens while they're away. It sort of keeps them aired and ready for the people when they come back and we take away a lot of catterpillers that eat the flowers cause we collect them and anyway they never know we've been there so it doesn't matter.

This garden of Genral Moult's had a flower bed with a lot of big stones on it that seemed to sort of spoil it and anyway we wanted them to make an island in the middle of his pond. It hadn't got an island and Ginger and me think that ponds look much better with islands in the middle. They made a jolly fine island and we had some jolly fine games with Ginger sittin on it being a lighthouse man and me captain of the ships that call at it to ask the time and suchlike. Then we made it into an island of robbers with me and Ginger the robber chief in turn and the other time the captain of a ship that goes to the island and gets captured.

Well, we were having great fun like this when suddenly Genral Moult came home and he got into a triffic temper, the sort of temper that people hold up to us as an awful warning if we don't learn to control ourselves when young, and I bet he'd

He didn't catch me, but he saw who I was, and shouted.

have killed us if we hadn't been too quick for him getting through the hole in the hedge.

Ginger got right away so he never knew who he was, but he saw me because I was a bit slower because I was on the island being the robber chief. He didn't catch me but he saw who I was and he shouted after me that he'd come and tell my father and that I'd ruined his rockerry and a lot more things that I'm tryin to remember for the next time I get into a temper with anyone. You'd think a flower bed'd look nicer without a lot of big stones stuck all over it, wouldn't you, and I think he ought to have been jolly grateful to us. But he'd said he was going to tell my father, and I wondered what to do because my father's the sort of man it would be impossible to make understand that me and Ginger had been helping Genral Moult and tryin to make his garden look nicer. You'd think a father would belive his own son instead of someone who's no relation to him at all wouldn't you? But my father never does.

Well, my father had gone away for a few days and the next day was the day my aunt had asked me to go to stay with her, so I suddenly thought that it would be a good plan to go away to my aunt because then when Genral Moult came to tell my father I'd be at my aunt's and he wouldn't be able to do anything to me and he might have forgotten when I came home.

So I went home and told my mother that I'd go to my aunt's and she said why and I said because she wanted me to and I wanted to do what she wanted me to do and she said that's a good boy and gave me a doughnut from a tin where I didn't know there were any because she's always changing the place she keeps them in. It made me rather sorry I was going away now I knew the place she was keepin them in, still it couldn't be helped and you can't have everything and I'd sooner miss my father and the doughnut than have both just then.

And now I reelly come to my aunt, and if youve got aunts I needn't tell you what she was like. I took a lot of trouble being polite to her but it didn't seem much use. She gave me just the same sort of food I get at home, meat an rice puddin and bread and butter and that dull sort of cake that people call holesum and just water or milk to drink, and at the end of the first day

When he got home his mother said he was not to play with me any more.

I began to wonder why people invited other people to stay with them if they were only going to give them the same sort of food to eat that they get at home.

There wasn't anything to do either. She said I could play in the garden if I didn't go on the lawn or the flower beds and that only left me the path to play on and when I did find a decent game to play on it pretendin to be a man makin a hole in the road she stopped me. She said I could play with the little son of a friend of hers and I taught him a jolly fine game pretending that a muddy place in a field was sinkin sands and one sinkin and the other rescuin in turns but when he got home his mother said he was not to play with me any more, and I didn't care because he'd been jolly rotten both at sinkin and rescuin and he said he'd rather have school than holidays so I knew he wouldn't be much good at anything.

When I'd been there three days my aunt said she was going to take me to a wist drive. I don't like drives genrally but I'd got so sick of my aunt's house and garden that I thought a drive would be rather fun so I said where are we goin to drive to an she said nowhere it's playing cards and I felt so fed up that if I'd known the way home I'd have gone. Then she said that wist means not talkin which made it sound jollier than ever (this is sarkasum). I hope she comes to stay with us sometime an I'll tell her we're goin to a circus and then when were just starting out I'll tell her that circus means goin to church an I bet shell be as mad as I was over that drive.

But I went to it with her and it was rotten. She'd taught me to play before we started out and I was jolly clever at learning it but I thought it was a silly sort of game and not half such fun as snap. They were all very bad tempered people playin at it, and I kept forgetting and playin snap because I'm more used to it and its a better game. They had what they call refreshments, but they didn't refresh me much, I can tell you, sandwiches so small that you could hardly see them and cakes no bigger than crumbs.

I'd got so fed up (and not with their refreshments let me tell you) that I lay awake all night till after ten o'clock wondering what to do to get home, and after thinkin about it all night like that till after ten I made up my mind that the only thing to do was to do something awful so that she'd send me home. So the next mornin after breakfast I set out to think of something awful to do, and the funny thing is that when you're trying to think of something awful to do you can't. Its a very funny thing and Ive often noticed it.

I sat and thought for nearly an hour an I couldn't think of anything reelly awful and at the end my aunt came out and said how good and quiet I was being and would I like to read a book that she'd had for a prize when she was a little girl called

I kept forgetting and playing snap, because I'm more used to it and it's a better game.

stories from histry, and that made me so fed up that I thought I'd go for a walk and see if I could think of anythin awful to do on the way because I'm one of those people that can think more walkin than I can sittin down.

I walked for ever so long thinking hard except once when I forgot and ran after a butterfly and jolly nearly caught it. I threw my cap and it ever so nearly got it but it just missed it and went into a pond instead an I thought it might as well stay there.

I was passing a house then, and I looked over the gate to see what sort of games you could play in the garden just like what everyone does when they're passin a house and no ones about, and suddenly I saw one of those garden beds with big stones in it and I thought of ole Genral Moult an how mad he'd got when I moved the stones out of his, and I thought I'd do it to this too, and this man would get mad and go and tell my aunt and she'd send me home.

There was no one about so I just went into the garden. There wasn't a pond to put the stones into but there was a lawn so I thought I'd put them all into the middle of the lawn. Just as I was goin to start I saw a man come in at the garden gate and unlock a side door of the house and go into it. He did it all in a quick sort of way and didn't look at the garden so I thought he must be one of those men that don't take any interest in their gardens and I didn't want to take all the trouble of movin the stones onto the grass if he wasn't goin to notice it. So then I had a jolly good idea, an I thought I'd put them all on the step of the door he'd just gon in so that he'd praps fall over them when he came out. That ought to make anyone mad enough to get anyone sent home.

So I took a lot of trouble moving them onto the step and then when I'd finished I sat down to wait till he came out again because I wanted him to know I'd done it, sos to be sure of getting sent home. Well soon he came back tryin to open the door. But it was a side door an it opened outwards, and he couldn't open it cause of the stones on the steps. I'd not thought of that because most doors open inwards, but of course it made it better cause he'd be madder than ever when he came out.

He didn't shout or anythin, he just kept on turning at the handle and pushin, but they were jolly heavy stones and it wasn't any use, and suddenly another man came and he said Hello what's all this and what are those stones doin there and whos in the house and I'd jus got as far as sayin well, I saw a man goin into the house – when he interrupted and pulled the stones away and dragged out a man and sent for a policeman, and when the policeman came he said that this man was a thief and that I'd seen him going into the house and must have put the stones there to keep him in sos he'd be caught cause I must have known that all the other doors and windows were fastened with burglar proof catches and that I was a very brave boy.

He gave me five shillings, and took me back to my aunt an told her how brave I'd been. Well, I didn't know what time it was (I once had a watch but Ginger spoilt it trying to turn it into a bomb with a bit of gunpowder) and I'd taken so long thinkin what to do that it was nearly tea time and my aunt had been so scared at me not comin in to lunch that she'd been out to look for me and she'd found my cap floatin on the pond and she'd gone to bed to have a nurvus breakdown and she had people fishing for me in the pond.

Well, she said she was too much upset to have me staying with her any longer so she mus send me home, and so she gave me five shillins to make up for the disappontment and wrote to my father telling him all about me havin been so brave catching a burglar and when I got home my father said he was very pleased with me and gave me two and six and said he'd let me off about Genral Moult's stones, and the day I got home was the day that Ethel and Robert were givin a picnic that they hadn't wanted me to go to and I went to it.

There was some jolly fine stuff to eat and I had a jolly fine tea and everyone wanted to hear about me capturing the burglar, and they all thought it was jolly fine and I ate six creams horns and there werent any left when Robert wanted one and I talked to all the girls that Robert wanted to talk to and to all the men that Ethel wanted to talk to and I had a jolly fine time.

So now if any of you want to get sent home from your aunts and have a jolly fine time as well, you know what to do.

My Day in London

Yes, of course I've been to London. I spent a whole day there only last month so I bet I know as much about London as anyone and I can jolly well tell you I don't think much of it. I never saw a place with so many shops and so many ladies. They're all over the place.

I should think it's just about the dullest place in the world. There aren't any trees to climb or gates to swing on and I didn't see a single field the whole day I was there. I can't think what people find to do in it all day. There aren't even any ditches to the roads. I did see some boys hanging on behind a lorry but they were the only people I saw enjoying themselves the whole day I was there and my aunt wouldn't let me go and do it with them. I bet I'd have hung on longer than any of them if she had. I saw one fall off. It was great fun watching.

I didn't know that my aunt was going to take me up to London till the morning. It was quite a surprise. She said that she was going to take me up for a birthday treat and that she'd take me to the Zoo and the British Museum. I said I didn't care much for music but she said it wasn't music it was statues. So I told her that I didn't much care for statues either but she said I'd like these. She said that everyone ought to see the British Museum and I said that I didn't want her to spend her money taking me there and she said she wasn't going to because you got in free and when I'd been there I jolly well wasn't surprised. Seems to me they ought to pay you for going there.

I thought I'd take one of my white rats up to London with me partly for company, because I knew my aunt wouldn't be much company, and partly to see exactly what sort of rat it was. I thought I'd go to the rat place in the Zoo and have a good look at them. I shouldn't be at all surprised to find that mine are really valuable rats because they're so clever. I stick bits of cheese through the bars at the top of their cage and they stand right up on their hind legs to get them. Well, they must be jolly clever to do that mustn't they? Not a bit like ordinary rats. Besides I thought he'd enjoy seeing all the other rats in the Zoo and he might find some of his relations there.

They made an awful fuss getting me ready. Worse than Sundays even. They kept sending me back to wash again and telling me I'd got a tide mark. I think I must have a sort of natural birth mark that looks like a tide mark because however much I wash they keep on telling me I've got one. It's very unfortunate for me. I shouldn't be surprised if in the end I get some sort of disease by washing and washing and washing away at my neck.

Then there's my knees. Some people naturally have light coloured knees and some people naturally have dark coloured knees just the same as some people naturally have light coloured hair and some people naturally have dark coloured hair and I naturally have the dark coloured sort of knees. It

They made an awful fuss getting me ready.

seems to me that it would be just as sensible to keep on telling a person with black hair to go on washing it till it went white as it is to keep on sending me back to wash my knees. Then there's my hair.

I dare say your hair grows along your head. A lot of people's hair grows along their head but mine doesn't. Mine grows up and it only wears it out trying to make it into the sort of hair that grows along. And anyway it seems to me that it's more natural for things to grow up same as trees and flowers and I like my hair to be natural. Anyway I was ready at last after hours and hours and hours of fuss that made me wonder whether London was going to be worth it because it would have to be jolly fine if it was and off we set. Fortunately no one had found out about my rat and he was in my pocket all right.

We had a very dull walk down to the station. My aunt kept telling me how lucky I was and how her aunts never took her up to London for the day when she was my age and when she wasn't saying that she was telling me to come out of the ditch and the hedge.

With her hurrying me along like that we got very early down to the station and she kept on at me just the same there telling me to come away from the edge of the platform and not to climb up the grass bank or jump on to the weighing machine thing. She wouldn't even let me get the cigarette packets from under the seat to see if anyone had left any cigarette cards in them. Well you've got to do something, haven't you? You can't do nothing. And there's nothing to do on a station but things like that.

The train came in at last and we got in and a whole lot of other people got in too. It was an awful squash. I bet that if it hadn't been such an awful squash my white rat would have kept quiet but there was a big fat woman sitting next to me and I bet she nearly squashed it flat. I didn't see it get out. It was the woman in the corner with the spectacles and the little hat that saw it first. She saw it running along the luggage rack thing.

Well it couldn't have done her any harm, could it? A little thing like a rat. She couldn't have made more fuss if it had been an elephant she'd seen running along the luggage thing instead of just a rat. And then they all began to carry on screaming and pushing each other about, trying to get behind each other and one of them even opened the carriage door to jump out and one tried to pull the little chain thing that makes the train stop but she got hystericks so bad that she couldn't pull it. I was rather

She couldn't have made more fuss if it had been an elephant instead of just a rat.

sorry about that because it would have been great fun to watch it stop. Then it disappeared and they didn't know where it had gone and they kept looking under the seats and in their baskets and thinking they saw it and beginning to scream again.

I'd seen it on the seat near me and slipped it back in my pocket without anyone seeing me. I bet it was jolly glad to get back there. They all kept saying what they were going to do about it. One of them was going to write to the railway company about it and another was going to write to Scotland Yard and another was going to write to the newspapers and another was going to write to her member of parliament. All of them were going to write to something. No one thought it was my rat because as soon as the fuss started I pretended to be asleep. I bet there's not many people that can pretend to be asleep as well as I can. It's a jolly useful thing to be able to do.

Well, then we got to London station. London station is a jolly big one ever so much bigger than ours at home but not so nice. It hasn't even got a grass bank like ours has that you can climb up and get through the railings at the top and it hasn't any flowers growing there at all. I bet it must have a jolly lazy station master. Ours grows the name of the station in flowers on the bank. London would be quite an easy word to grow in flowers so I bet it's just laziness. And the porters aren't so nice as ours. They don't seem to take any interest in you. I tried pulling a face at one and he didn't take any notice. It makes ours wild when you pull faces at him. Once he ran after me right out of the station and all down the road. I bet it would be jolly dull living in London.

My aunt seemed a bit tired and cross though I don't know what she'd got to be tired and cross about. She kept on asking me about that rat as if she'd got a sort of suspicion it was mine but I kept saying 'What rat?' as if I'd been asleep all the time so in the end she gave it up. But she said that it had been a very trying journey and she must go and have some strong coffee before she did anything else. So I said all right and we went.

She picked out quite a nice cake shop and she told the waitress she'd like a cup of coffee and a plain bun and she asked me if I was hungry and would like a plain bun. I said I was hungry but wouldn't like a plain bun. After all we ought to be truthful before polite. So she sighed, though I don't know what she'd got to sigh about, and told me to choose a cake from the window while she went to wash her hands. So I did.

I chose a jolly fine cake very big and made to look just like a cauliflower with green marzipan stuff outside and full of cream inside. It was a jolly fine cake. When she came back I was half way through it and she said that she hadn't meant that sort of a cake at all and it would make me sick. I didn't argue with her. I just went quietly on with it and proved to her that it wouldn't make me sick. It takes more than a little thing like that to upset me. You'd hardly believe some of the things I've eaten. I'd finished it before she'd finished her plain bun. It was a jolly dull sort of plain bun. It hadn't even got currants in. It's surprising to me the things grown ups choose to eat when they might have anything.

Then she said we'd better be getting on to the Zoo so we did. If ever you want to go to the Zoo don't go with my aunt. She won't go into the lion place because it gives her a headache and she won't go into the monkey place because she says they're vulgar and she won't go into the bear place because she says it's dangerous and she won't go into the snake pit because she says it makes her feel faint and she won't go into the parrot place because she says they use bad language and she won't go into the fish place because you have to pay.

We did go into the fish place in the end and they're all exactly like people you know and I've never laughed so much in all my life. I laughed so much they nearly turned me out. She let me have a ride on the elephant too but it wasn't a success because my white rat got out again. Well, you wouldn't think that people that have come to the Zoo to see savage animals would be scared by a little thing like a rat, would you? But they are. You'd never believe the fuss those people on the elephant's back made when that rat got out among them. Screaming to the man to stop at once and things like that. I caught it and put it away jolly quick but they made me get down and you'd have thought I'd murdered them the way they went on at me. I couldn't help hoping that a lion or a tiger would get loose and come after them just to teach them a lesson. I bet they'd jolly well wish it was my rat after them instead then.

My aunt knew that it was my rat of course after that and she wasn't much nicer about it than the people on the elephant. But she didn't know what to do about it. She couldn't tell me to throw it away because it would have made all the people round carry on same as the people in the railway carriage and on the elephant so she told me to keep it in my pocket and she said she'd tell the first policeman we met to take it from me. I knew she wouldn't but I couldn't help rather hoping she would because he couldn't take it to the police station till he went home at night and it would be great fun to watch a policeman stopping motor cars and things with a white rat in one hand. And it might have bitten him which would be more fun still.

Anyway she didn't and we went to have dinner. I was jolly hungry because it was half past one and I'd had nothing to eat since that cake at eleven. My aunt made me have meat first but she said I could choose what I liked for pudding so I chose pineapple cream and trifle and cream and apple tart and cream and cream buns and ice cream.

My aunt didn't seem to eat much. She said she wasn't very hungry.

Then we went to the British Museum. If any of you are thinking of going to the British Museum I can jolly well tell you that it's not worth going to. It's full of great huge broken statues and nothing else. You'd think they'd have got someone to mend them up a bit, wouldn't you? Or else thrown them away and got some new ones. There must have been lots of rummage sales they could have sent them to since they got broke. I soon had enough of going round with my aunt and my aunt saying the date they were made and who made them and things like that and soon I met another boy going round with his aunt and his aunt telling him the dates they were made and who made them and that sort of thing.

He pulled a face at me as soon as he saw me and it was nearly as good a face as the best one I pull so I knew he was all right. We managed to get our aunts into crowds and then we managed to get off together and then we had great fun. The Museum is a jolly good place to have games in. We played a sort of Hide and Seek at first till a very cross man stopped us and then we played a game the boy had made up. It's a fine game. Whenever you see several people together you go up and stand near them and begin talking to each other and saying that you've just had Scarlet Fever and your mother said it wouldn't do you any harm to come out though the doctor said you ought to stay another week. Then you watch them all making off in all directions.

It's great fun. We did it with heaps of them. It's one of the nicest of that sort of game that I've ever played. Then we saw

If any of you are thinking of going to the British Museum, I can jolly well tell you that it's not worth going to.

a lot of them having a sort of lesson in front of one of those big old broken statues and a man with a stick was telling them about it and pointing to it with his stick. The boy was carrying my rat (he was awfully fond of rats and he'd got 30 of his own at home) and he went behind the statue and put the rat on it and it ran up it and just as the man was pointing to the top of the statue and saying 'notice the beautiful head-dress on this statue', the rat suddenly came out on the statue's head where he was pointing and all the women screamed and went off. But of course the boy and me couldn't stay to see much more of it because we had to clear off quick.

The annoying part of it was that when we went back afterwards we couldn't find the rat anywhere and when our aunts found us we still hadn't found the rat. So my rat's still in the British Museum. If any of you go there you might have a look for it. My aunt seemed to think that it was her fault she'd lost me because she was so interested in the statues and so did the boy's aunt so that was all right. Then the boy and his aunt went off and the boy pulled a jolly fine face just as they were going. He was a jolly nice boy. My aunt was glad to hear that my rat was lost and got me out as soon as she could in case I found it again. Then we went to have tea. She let me have poached eggs for tea because I was jolly hungry because it was after five and I'd had nothing to eat since dinner.

Then she took me on the top of a bus pointing out all the buildings and telling me what they were. They all looked the same to me and I couldn't take any interest in them. They all looked dull and as if you couldn't have any fun in them. I wouldn't have swopped our barn for any of them.

Then we went back to London station and then we went home and I was jolly glad to get back to a decent place with hedges and ditches and trees to climb and animals and things like that. I can't think why anyone lives in London. I suppose that it's only very poor people who can't afford to live in the country.

My aunt didn't say much to my mother when she took me back except that she'd had a very tiring day.

My mother says I ought to give my aunt a little present to remind her of our day together.

I think I'll give her a white rat.

I'll Tell You What's Wrong with Christmas

A man came to our school last term to lecture about reforms. He said that reforms meant putting things right what were wrong. He said that in the old days there weren't any schools, and then reformers came along and made them.

I think they'd've done better leavin' things like that alone.

That's where I think reformers have gone wrong all the time. They change things that don't need to be changed an' they leave things alone that ought to be changed. Hundreds of years ago there wasn't any schools or museums or dancin' classes or savin's banks – not till reformers came along an' made them.

What I think is that there ought to be some reformers for reformin' reformers.

What I partic'ly want to tell you about is reformin' Christmas. Fancy reformers goin' about all these years interferin' with things that were perfectly all right an' makin' things like schools that nobody wanted an' not tryin' to reform Christmas. Why, Christmas is all wrong from beginnin' to end.

If I started reformin' Christmas, I'd start at the very beginnin' an' go on reformin' till I'd got to the end.

First of all I wun't let the shops shut on Christmas Day.

People come along an' give you money for a Christmas present knowin' quite well that you can't go out an' spend it right away, an' then they go on an' on at you all day 'bout savin' it till like as not by the end of the day they've got you to put it in a nasty ole money-box what it's difficult to get it out of, or give it to someone to keep for you what it's very difficult

89

to get it back from, while if the shops were open you could have gone straight out an' spent it before they'd finished breakfast.

They've got you to put it in a nasty ole money-box.

Why, I've known an extreme case of meanness where a poor boy was given some money in a *locked* money-box what his aunt kept the key of. That's the sort of thing what ought to be stopped by law.

If I was a king, I'd make a law that no one was to mention money boxes or savin' on Christmas Day, and anyone what mentioned a money box or savin' was to be put in prison for a year an' that the shops were to be left open.

Then, of course, there's presents. Aunts, of course, are worse than anyone at this. Why, I've known an extreme case of a poor boy what had for sole Christmas presents a pair of socks, a pair of braces, a nail-brush and a prayer book.

Now, it's extr'ordin'ry to me that folks get sent to prison for jus' signin' each other's names an' little things like that, an' an aunt can give things like that for Christmas presents an' nothin' happen to her.

An' the worst isn't havin' things like that given to you. It's havin' to be grateful for them. We read in books that it's the nature an' duty of parents to protect their children, but no one would think so on Christmas Day.

When a poor child is given – say, a pyjama case or a tin of tooth paste – you'd expect the parent to fling it back in the aunt's or uncle's face that gave it, an' *insist* on them changin' it for a mouth organ or a catapult or an air-gun or a bow an' arrows.

But they don't.

They smile jus' as if the things were real presents, 'stead of insults, an' say, '*Very* kind of you. *Isn't* it kind of her, dear? Say, "Thank you," to her, dear.' An' you've got to say it, or worse will follow.

An' you'd hardly believe it, but it's true – when people do give *real* presents an' you'd think the parents would be glad for their poor children to get jus' a little pleasure – if you'd believe *me* – they're not at all pleased.

They screw up their faces an' say, 'How kind of you, but – perhaps I'd better keep this for you, dear, till you're a little older. You know, Aunt Jane's staying with us and she doesn't like noise,' or, 'You remember what happened when you had that other catapult.'

I've known an extreme case.

Parents' memories are the most extr'ordin'ry things. If it's anythin' you particular want them to remember, they forget it, an' if it's anythin' you particular want them to forget they remember it. When they've def'nitely promised – said *quite* def'nitely, 'I'll think about it,' which counts as a def'nite promise – to let you have your friends in for a nice quiet little talk in the garden, it's 's likely as not they'll forget all about it, or say that they didn't def'nitely promise.

But when it's a question of a small hole made in a cucumber frame or a slight break in a window or jus' a little thing like that not worth mentioning, they go on remembering it long after you've forgotten it.

In books one reads a lot about the wonderful love an' kindness of parents for their children, but all the parents I've come across in real life have been most intensely unnatural.

To return to the Christmas presents an' bein' made to say, 'Thank you,' for things you haven't any gratitude in your heart for. What I mean to say is our parents send us to Sunday school to learn to speak the truth an' then they themselves force us to say, 'Thank you,' for things we haven't any gratitude in our hearts for.

The poor boy what was given the braces an' made to say 'Thank you' for them felt so bitter about it that he made them into a catapult an' got a good deal of pleasure from it till his parents found out, then the poor boy was treated by them in a very cruel fashion.

Now you know what I feel about Christmas presents. There ought to be def'nite laws about it, an' anyone what gives useless things like clothes an' boots an' tooth-brushes or things like that ought to be put in prison, an' parents that makes their poor child say 'Thank you' for things what he hasn't any gratitude in his heart for should be obliged to pay a very large fine, which should go to the poor child.

Then there's the rest of Christmas. Reformers ought to start on it right away.

One may not go out to play with one's friends.

One is told that one must stay in to talk to aunts and uncles who really do not wish to talk to one any more than one wishes to talk to them.

I've known an extreme case of a poor boy whose aunt not only gave him a hair-brush for a Christmas present but also read a book of English History to him all Christmas afternoon.

This terrible treatment, of course, drove the poor boy to put the hair brush in her bed and dress up as a ghost to frighten her, but he was treated in a very cruel fashion by his parents when they found out.

One is also told that one must not make a noise. I think that one of the new laws reforming Christmas ought to be that everyone must make a noise jus' to help keep things cheerful and that those who do not should pay large fines which should go to those who do.

I will now start and go right through the day telling you all

Just to help keep things cheerful.

the things that ought to be altered in it. It begins with getting up. What I notice is that though grown-ups are fond of talking about early rising, and saying what a fine thing it is for a boy, they don't seem pleased when you rise early on Christmas Day.

On the days when there's nothing in particular to get up for, they talk a lot about it, but on Christmas Day, when you nat'rally want to get up early to see whether you've had any better luck with presents than you had last year, they seem to take quite a different view.

On Christmas Day I have often got up as early as three o'clock in the morning and started playing CHRISTIANS AWAKE! on mouth organs and things just to help make things nice and jolly for the other people in the house, but no one has ever shown me the least gratitude.

Pers'nally, I think it would be a good thing if people didn't go to bed the night before Christmas. I never feel that I want to go to bed, and I've often thought that I could get a good deal of fun out of staying up all night.

Perhaps, though, it would be as well if the grown-ups went to bed but not the children. One often hears grown-ups saying that Christmas is the children's day, and yet no grown up has ever taken my advice about how to make it jollier for the children.

I think we could have a very fine time indeed staying up all night while the grown-ups are in bed.

Breakfast, of course, comes next. Breakfast on Christmas morning is spoilt by there being too many grown ups, and all of them talking too much. A poor child finds it almost impossible to make his voice heard, and is not treated with much encouragement when he does.

Immediately after breakfast the grown-ups start straight away spoiling your pleasure by making you go to Church so that you cannot play with whatever presents you have.

I have sometimes tried to overcome this difficulty by taking some of my smaller presents to church with me, but I do not really recommend this.

Clockwork things have a way of going off when you don't expect them to, and some of those balloon pig things, though quite easy to blow up without anyone noticing, are quite difficult when they start going down. If you are very careful, of course, you can take your sweets to church with you, though I remember a very painful occasion when my father sat upon some chocolate creams which I had put down upon the seat and forgotten about.

It was the beginning of the Second Lesson and, of course, he had to wait till the end before he could start trying to get them off, and, by that time, they had soaked in. The church is always decorated for Christmas, but in a very dull way. Christmas decorations are not half as interesting as Harvest Festival decorations. I sometimes find Harvest Festival decorations very interesting indeed.

Then, of course, we go home to dinner. I have nothing against dinner, except the interference of the grown-ups.

The afternoon of Christmas Day, I think, might be improved in many ways. It is extr'ordin'ry to me that grown-ups after sleeping hard all night, and showing themselves most disagreeable when awakened by a Christmas hymn (which one would think would fill them with joy and gratitude), should want to go up to their bedrooms to sleep again directly after dinner.

Aunts and uncles, of course, are the worst for this. And one would, of course, be very glad for them to go up to their bedrooms for the afternoon if only they did not complain and say that the slightest little noise was disturbing them.

I think that grown-ups ought to try to harden themselves to such little sounds as drums and tin trays and air-guns and whistling and singing and Indian war cries.

It seems to me that if soldiers can learn to sleep with the noise of guns all around them then grown-ups ought to be able to sleep with those little sounds I have mentioned going on around them. All concerned would be much happier if they would. It has always struck me as strange that grown-ups should be so mad when roused from sleep by some little sound. I myself feel like that.

It is extr'ordin'ry to me that it is the custom to have crowds of aunts and uncles staying with us at Christmas, because I cannot help thinking that they would be much happier in their own homes where they could sleep quietly all the day if they wanted to.

I think that it would be far better to have boys staying in the house instead.

I would not at all mind inviting a few nice quiet boys like Ginger and Douglas and Henry to stay with us for Christmas, and then I think the whole thing would be much jollier.

Then in the evening comes a play or an entertainment. This is always got up entirely by one's elder sister and brother and their friends who use their age and strength to stop you enjoying it or helping in any way. I have often tried to help my brother and sister and their friends to make the play or entertainment a success, but they have on each occasion treated me with base ingratitude.

On one occasion I very kindly came on to do a few conjuring tricks in an interval, and they complained bitterly afterwards that they kept slipping on the yolks of eggs on the carpet. It is true that the eggs which should have appeared in my friend's pocket kept dropping on to the floor, but this was the fault of the book, as I carried out the instructions quite carefully.

There was also a certain amount of trouble on the same occasion about a watch which I borrowed from an uncle, and which the directions in the book told me to 'appear to smash with a hammer' and which was then to be discovered whole in his pocket.

It is more difficult than it sounds to appear to smash something with a hammer, and the watch mender said when he took it to him the next day that he was afraid that nothing could be done about it. I think that perhaps the hammer was too big, but as I said at the time (but no one listened to me because they were so busy talking themselves) it is only through mistakes like that that one learns.

Then there was another occasion when my sister was singing a song, and I thought it would be a very nice idea to accompany her behind the scenes with my new trumpet and drum. I learnt from her afterwards that she did not agree with me.

After this comes dancing. It is extr'ordin'ry to me what fun grown-ups can find in their kind of dancing, just walking round a room with a silly ole girl. War dances, of course, are quite different.

The only decent part of Christmas is the food, and even that is spoilt by grown-ups. It is very cruel and un-Christian to stop boys eating as much as they want to on Christmas simply because they happened to have been rather ill the Christmas before. Parents should remember that one is a year older than one was last year, and cons'quently can eat a good deal more.

I think that if Christmas was reformed in the way I have said, everyone would be much happier. I know I should.